A PRACTICAL GUIDE TO HEALTH AND SAFETY IN THE ENTERTAINMENT INDUSTRY

Marco van Beek

D0582963

ENTERTAINMENT TECHNOLOGY PRESS

Safety Series

The only purpose for which power can be rightfully
exercised over any member of a civilised community,
against his will, is to prevent harm to others.
His own good, either physical or moral, is not
a sufficient warrant.

On Liberty - John Stuart Mill

A PRACTICAL GUIDE TO HEALTH AND SAFETY IN THE ENTERTAINMENT INDUSTRY

Marco van Beek

Entertainment Technology Press

A Practical Guide to Health and Safety in the Entertainment Industry
© Marco van Beek

First publication September 2000

A title in continuous publication within the
Entertainment Technology Press Safety Series
Series editor: John Offord

Published by Entertainment Technology Press Ltd
The Studio, High Green, Great Shelford, Cambridge, CB2 5EG
Internet: www.etnow.com

Series Code: PGHS / 002 / 03-01

FOREWORD

I heard a report on the radio recently that fatal accidents in the construction industry had increased by 20% in recent years. Furthermore, these incidents were not confined to small 'cowboy' outfits; many accidents are happening on large sites run by giant construction companies. This is alarming. With new building techniques and increasingly sophisticated mechanical handling plant you would expect accidents to decrease, wouldn't you? I worked as a hod carrier on several building sites in student vacations (and when 'resting' in the early days of my professional career) and I remember that conditions were very primitive indeed and many of the manual labouring practices quite precarious.Forty years later it seems almost inconceivable that, whilst general conditions have clearly improved, the safety situation has apparently worsened. Is profit being put before safety? Is it the result of simple complacency? Or is it due to the replacement of manual tasks by mechanisation?

In our own industry we have added dangers. Extreme fatigue has become a way of life. Our structures are by definition only temporary and we are constantly pushing the innovation envelope. Schedules are tight and urgency prevails over all things - the show must go on after all. There are no accurate statistics but there is a general feeling that our rapidly growing industry has fared quite well - so far. This is a tribute to all the production personnel out there. Maybe we just got lucky - so far. There have been a few fatal accidents recently and there is certainly no room for complacency.

Marco's book is an essential piece of reading. His direct style of writing cuts through a lot of the mumbo jumbo and gobbledygook. He brings with him the advantages of practical experience; you can tell he has been there and done it. This guide neatly summarises the whole complicated issue and lists further, drier, reading for those that need it. Everybody engaged in our industry should have easy access to a copy of Marco's 'Practical Guide'.

Live long - be healthy - be safe!

Brian Croft, Chairman, Vari-Lite London.
London, September 2000

CONTENTS

1 INTRODUCTION

This book is designed to provide a practical approach to Health and Safety within the Live Entertainment and Event industry. It seeks to clarify the relationships between promoters, production managers, contractors and sub-contractors, freelancers, venues and the public.

It will give industry-pertinent examples, that everyone in the Live Event sector can relate to, and it seeks to break down the myths surrounding Health & Safety into easily manageable morsels. For too long the 'smoke and mirrors' surrounding the uniqueness of the industry have prevented us looking at the problems in stark daylight.

It is my experience that we are not an 'unsafe' industry, but there is a belief outside our ivory tower that we are just a bit cavalier about safety. Because there is an overall lack of documentation, we cannot disprove the theories that four-fifths of our accidents never get reported. The Construction Industry has had a unique set of regulations (Construction: Design & Management, - also known as CDM) imposed on it because of a similar attitude. Whilst CDM is actually quite a good solution for some of our larger scale events, it is not something we want imposed on us at every level.

Because of the way the Health & Safety Executive is funded, they are unlikely to act until there is a major incident. By then it is too late, and the whole industry could be tainted. If we are seen as irresponsible and unfit to manage our own affairs, the fallout may jeopardise the industry, and I, for one, have no desire to have to go and get a 'real' job.

Readers of this book must be aware that it is based on current UK legislation, applicable at the time of writing. Whilst it will serve as a useful guideline, I would encourage people to read the regulations themselves. There have been too many instances of 'chinese whispers' over the years that have been not only misleading, but dangerous. If in doubt, go the the relevant regulations first.

European law is slowly being harmonised across the EU. The intention is to end up with a level playing field, but different countries have started from different positions. In the long run, it should all become a lot easier.

Internationally, there are too many variations to enable an all-embracing book to be written. However, a safe working practice should be safe anywhere - if it was safe in the first place. Serious and sensible documentation, whether it conforms to a local standard or not, proves that your intentions are honourable.

2 THE PERCEPTION OF SAFETY

We all have differing opinions, and we all have differing viewpoints. So why should the issue of safety be any different? When looking at the same thing from a different angle we will see something the other person doesn't. And because of all these differing viewpoints, we tend to have our own opinion on what is safe and what isn't. Worst of all, there is a natural tendency to assume that everyone else sees things the same way.

Most accidents are caused by omission rather than by a deliberate act - by someone 'forgetting' to check something, leaving a box or cable in someone else's way. We assume too much. We should never assume that we know more than someone else, but nor should we assume that they know more than us. We all have to do things for the first time, but how many of us ask (or tell) first?

In any industry, facing change will always bring resistance and the fact that the subject of health and safety is catching up with us makes us feel that it is new. It isn't, but that doesn't make us feel any better about it. There will always be people who thought the old ways were better, that it is all a waste of time. Luckily for our industry, there are people who have always believed we could do better.

The point is that Health and Safety legislation is there for our benefit and protection, and has not been introduced as a personal vendetta by some dark overlord. However, it also works on the same basic principles as the concept of liberty. My freedom stops where someone else's begins. Morally, I should not do something that will adversely affect others. As a society we have decided that laws must be put in place to protect the many from the few.

'Health and Safety' is a mindset, it is not a way of life. It is a general aware-ness that everything we do can, and will, affect others. Apart from the legal obligations placed upon us, there are strong moral reasons why we should try and prevent harm to others, in addition to the hope that they will do the same to us.

Because accidents are just that, accidents, there is an assumption that by the time they happen, it is too late to do anything. In physics, Newton's Law tells us that to every action there is an equal and opposite reaction. In safety, every action has a consequence. It is very easy to try and blame someone else, but since there is rarely any malice involved, this is out of place. However, what we must learn is that an accident always has a *reason* for happening. Every accident is theoretically preventable in some way.

So what is this 'mindset'? It is a combination of moral responsibility and peer pressure. It is the concept that it is part of your role in life to prevent injury to others. It is an obligation never to just walk past something that you know is unsafe. It may be as simple as a loose hook clamp, or a safety bond that has been forgotten. You find an unattended screwdriver on the truss - you take it off and put it somewhere safe. It wasn't your 'job', it wasn't your screwdriver, you might never have to walk on stage and under where that tool may fall, but a simple act, that takes seconds of your time, may have arrested a chain of events that may have caused an injury.

It is this mindset that requires us to be clear about our instructions to others. Do we lift 'on three' or 'after three'? It is this mindset that makes us pause and think about our actions, about engaging the brain before the muscle, and to always think about the bigger picture.

Every one of us has the power to make this industry safer, even if it is just by a small degree. Mark up a bad cable before it is returned to the warehouse, so that the person at the other end spots it, assigning specific duties to people rather than assuming they know what is going on. Carpenters talk about measuring twice and cutting once. Think about it . . .

You will find that in your professional capacity, you will form opinions on what you consider to be safe. Properly documented, this becomes a 'professional opinion', and whilst we may argue about that opinion, there will be times when only you can make that call. As a competent professional, your opinion is backed up by experience and knowledge. When a number of professionals get together and combine their 'opinions' they can create 'codes of practice'. Our industry does that - the Event Safety Guide and BS7909 are but two examples, written for us, by us, and nationally recognised.

3 RESPONSIBILITIES

Overview

In simple terms, the person who stands to gain most from a show, is usually the person or company who has the control over the largest chunk of money. This means that they also have ultimate control over how the money is spent, and therefore, ultimately responsible for choosing the venue, contractors and crew, and how safe they are.

You cannot delegate responsibility unless you also delegate authority. Someone who is not allowed to choose how the money is spent cannot be held responsible for the outcome.

'Employer' and 'Employee'

The terms of 'employer' and 'employee' are constantly referred to within Health and Safety legislation, and one must be aware that there are subtle but crucial differences in the definitions of these terms as opposed to the ones used by the Inland Revenue.

As far as the tax man is concerned, it is all to do with when (and where) the tax is paid. An 'employee' is PAYE, and pays tax at source, and an employer pays additional National Insurance for every employee on their books. A 'Self Employed' person (also known as a Freelancer or 'Schedule D') is outside of this loop.

When it comes to Health and Safety, there is no third way. You are either an Employer, an Employee, or both. Each has a responsibility to the other, and in most cases, to other employers and employees within the same event.

Promoters

The promoter holds a key position within the industry. The person (or company) carrying out this role is the kingpin to the success of the whole venture. They must balance the requirements and costs of all the different contracting companies, artists and venues, while always ensuring a spectacle worthy of the ticket price. However, as this central point, the promoter is also at the top of the ladder, the person with ultimate responsibility, and the person who, in the case of an accident, could be sent to jail.

Production Managers

The 'Production Manager' (other terms are used in different areas of the industry) is the person with the day-to-day responsibility for Health and Safety. The load-in schedule, call times (and length of call times) for crew, availability of fork lift trucks, cherry-pickers and catering are all down to them, and their staff.

Whilst many risks and hazards can be identified before the start of an event, it is the Production Manager who is in the unique situation of seeing and controlling most activities. This is the person who needs to communicate to all the staff and crew the details of those hazards that may affect all of the people involved in the production.

As an example, the noise levels associated with the sound check may be a risk to a lighting technician who is trying to focus. Prior warning of the time of the sound check would mean that the technician could either leave it to another time, or use ear defenders or an intercom system. Without this information, the technician may be in a position of not being able to communicate reliably with the rest of the lighting crew, and an accident could occur.

Venues

The venue, even if it is a green field-site, is a workplace, and therefore there are minimum legal requirements not only for the public who will attend, but also for the crew. Toilets, wash areas, changing rooms, rest areas and other facilities are all required by law for the crew, from the moment they arrive.

If the venue is an established building, all these requirement are normally in place, but access is not always automatic. Locked toilets and fire doors are common in these times of increasing theft and vandalism, and work lights are often inadequate for the complex work and inspections that are carried out during a load-in and load-out.

Contractors

Contractors are the suppliers employed by the production/promoter to provide equipment and services. They, in turn, have employees within their organisation who may arrive on site to carry out a task. At this point a division of authority and responsibility occurs. The employing company is responsible for the safety of its employees, but other than their crew, has little or no presence on site. The production manager is responsible for the day-to-day safety of the site, and all the people on it.

The relationship between the contracting company, its crew, and the production manager becomes complex, but in simple terms, it all comes down to communication. The production manager must treat the contractor's crew as employees of the production, passing on the same information as to the rest of the crew. However, the contracted company must ensure that their crew are properly trained and equipped for the job. The contracted company must also satisfy themselves that they are not sending their staff into the middle of an unsafe environment, and to empower their staff to refuse to work in unsafe conditions, knowing that they have the full backing of the company.

Crew Chiefs

Even if you are a freelancer, if you are a crew chief you are also an 'employer' as well as an 'employee'. Crew chiefs have a responsibility in ensuring that the people working for them are protected from hazards, that risk assessments have been carried out and that safe working practices are in place, and followed.

Sub Contractors and Freelancers

In most cases, a subcontractor and a freelancer are the same thing. The main issue being whether someone is 'self-employed' or an 'employee'. Even without being on PAYE, some people are employees, and this must be identified to the person or company who is contracting you for the work.

A true 'self employed' person is a company in all but name. They take business risks, invest in tools and equipment, have public liability insurance, have properly printed headed notepaper and invoices, use an accountant and have day-to-day business expenses and overheads such as telephones, faxes and email.

An employee has none of these, and relies on the employer for all their equipment and tools, hard hats and harnesses. If you expect your employer to provide everything, then they also have a right (and an obligation, under some guidelines referred to by the Inland Revenue as IR35) to pay you on a PAYE basis.

As an employee, the employer does almost everything for you. As a self-employed person you take over that responsibility. Having a harness checked regularly, training and insurance are all duties to be performed. There is no halfway measure. As a self-employed person you are both the employee and the employer.

Summary

It is important to realise that no one is exempt from the issues raised in this book. No matter where you fit into the chain, you have responsibilities to every other person involved in the event. From alerting the Production Manager to a potential hazard, to planning a safe lift of a lighting rig, you have responsibilities. Even if you are just an equipment supplier, you have a duty to ensure that the equipment is safe and fit for purpose, and that the user (or purchaser) is told about any hazards they may not be aware of.

4 SAFETY POLICY

Overview

The purpose of a Safety Policy is to lay out the methods by which the company (or production) intends to ensure a safe (and healthy) working environment. Within its covers should be all the information needed by all 'employees', such as the nearest hospital, who the first-aiders are, or how to get hold of them, who the responsible persons are, how to raise the alarm in case of fire, special rules, such as visitors and lone working, and any special training needed. The Safety Policy can be broken down into a number of areas.

General Statement of Policy

This statement is the smallest, and most legally binding part of any Safety Policy. It is a declaration (in the case of a company) signed by the managing director. In the case of a production, it should be the person who has the highest authority, usually the promoter.

The declaration is a statement of acceptance of ultimate responsibility. The signatory has complete control over all budgetary considerations that may have an influence on the overall safety of the project in hand. This is where the buck stops.

The statement also clearly identifies any other persons who have been assigned direct responsibilities, such as training, safety inspections, carrying out accident investigations, as well as the general responsibilities of all employees, supervisors and managers.

General Arrangements

The section on general arrangements covers the information required on a day-to-day basis by all persons within the workplace. In most cases in our industry, it can be easier to break it down into three areas, not all of which will apply to everybody.

Warehouse/Office: This area covers the normal office and warehouse duties of the full time staff and freelancers who come in to prepare equipment. The company has full control of the work environment, is responsible for the fire certificate, first aid, and all the other 'normal' health and safety issues.

On Site / On the Road: Crew working on site is often an easier task to cover, because of the limited responsibility to the general fabric of the building, and is therefore usually limited to issues concerning the equipment and tasks carried out.

Venues: The hardest part of all is when the general public are allowed into a building. While in an office, visitors can be accompanied by a staff member to prevent them from getting into a hazardous area, or from becoming a hazard themselves. Any building with a 'rentable' space needs special consideration in respect of the people using it.

Accidents

The Safety Policy must identify the arrangements for First Aid including location of first aid boxes, who is (or how to contact) a qualified first-aider, the person charged with maintaining the first aid boxes, and the reporting of incidents (RIDDOR).

Fire Safety

The Safety Policy will lay out how the alarm is raised, how the building is to be evacuated, maintenance and location of fire fighting equipment, maintained lighting and persons responsible for checking escape routes and head counts.

Advice and Consultation

All the Health and Safety legislation recognises the need for advice and consultation on the convoluted topics that may arise. It is therefore perfectly acceptable to have any number of external people and bodies from whom the company gets advice. It is important for these people to be noted in the Safety Policy, in case they need to be contacted. The most important person on this list is usually the local safety officer, who may be from either the HSE themselves, or most usually, from the local authority concerned. However, you must note that you cannot absolve yourself from your responsibilities simply by hiring a consultant.

Training

A significant number of accidents are proven to have been preventable, if only adequate training had been provided. Having a training plan, managed by a senior member of the company, is very important. Keeping details of all training, even internal, is very important so that you can prove due diligence in the event of an accident.

If you are a freelancer, list your skills and deficiencies and what training you would benefit from. You may even be able to find someone willing to fund you, such as the DSS or various training establishments.

Rules for Contractors and Visitors

All these rules are usually laid down for the full time members of staff who are in the building most of the time. However, from time to time, visitors and contractors will appear at your door. There may be serious (but contained) hazards present which they will be completely unaware of. Their presence could trigger an event that was unforeseen, simply because they didn't know the 'rules'.

You may decide that visitors can be safely let loose in the office, but must be accompanied in the warehouse. Contractors (e.g. the local plumber) may need to be told about certain ground rules before being left alone. There is no sense in putting rules in place if they are never going to be followed because they are impractical. On the other hand, simple things like stopping people from carrying drinks into the three-phase test bay or the under-stage dimmer city are simple and understandable.

Hazards

The Safety Policy must identify the location of certain information and procedures. These include risk assessments, chemical datasheets, electrical maintenance records and other safety inspections. The following areas need consideration.

Documentation

Certain documentation may be needed in a hurry. Stating clearly where hazard data sheets and manuals are to be kept may save a lot of time when a life is at stake.

Housekeeping and Premises

An untidy workplace will always create more hazards than necessary. Apart from the obvious fire risks of rubbish, other areas may not be as apparent, and the purpose of the Safety Policy is to clarify responsibilities, duties, and share information.

Cleanliness: Set specific responsibilities and duties for each work area, and ensuring they are carried out.

Waste Disposal: Clarify as to who provides the rubbish collection, and what can't be thrown into the bin could prevent a prosecution under environmental regulations. Simple rules about aerosol canisters, paint, oil, etc should therefore be easily found easily by all personnel.

Safe Stacking and Storage: You may have a racking system with a weight rating, or the flightcases you use shouldn't be stacked more than two high.

Gangways and Exits: A fire exit is usually an area where junk collects. Having them clearly marked and inspection duties assigned can help prevent the situation of a blocked exit and the major problem of escape from a burning building.

Access Equipment (ladders, etc): If your staff use ladders, moveable stairs, etc in the course of their duties, they must be regularly checked to make sure they are safe.

Electrical Safety

Most people have heard about Portable Appliance Testing (PAT), but all electrical equipment must be regularly inspected. Even the building wiring should be checked every few years. The kettle, fridge and microwave could all fail and hurt a staff member, and not just the rental stock.

Machinery

All machinery is dangerous. We all know that guards should be fitted, goggles worn and gloves used. More than this, the equipment should be checked to make sure it is still safe, that safety cut-outs are still connected, and shafts are within tolerance, etc. The manufacturers' manuals will lay out servicing and visual checks.

Lifting Equipment: Lifting Equipment comes under special regulations (referred to as LOLER), and an inspection schedule should be drawn up. This has to cover not only chain hoists, but steel ropes, spansets, shackles, etc.

Work equipment: The provision of work equipment, also has its own regulations - PUWER. These cover any tools and equipment provided by the employer, from screwdrivers to forklifts.

Dangerous Substances

In any workplace, we will find any number of dangerous substances. Chemicals which we will happily buy for our own home can suddenly become a safety nightmare. Every chemical used in a business must be assessed for usage, safe disposal, first aid measures, spillage control, flammability and PPE (Personal Protective Equipment).

Fluids under Pressure

The presence of a fluid (which includes air) under pressure is a risk in itself. Irresponsible use of compressed air can blind someone, even if all the tools are properly maintained.

Software Issues

Hopefully we have all got through the other side of the Millennium by the time you are reading this, so why are we still concerned? Well, the Y2K 'bug' highlighted a number of issues that should always be in the back of your mind when buying or building a piece of equipment.

Software writers, just like their literary counterparts, are not infallible. For any piece of code there will be a number of mistakes. Some will be a nuisance, some could be catastrophic. Having a computer freeze up on you may sound trivial, but it might be the one flying the plane you're in. Technology is getting more complex, and the key to safety is simplicity. These two goals are unreconcilable. If safety is an issue, remember the 1st January, 2000 (and 09/09/1999, and 29/02/2000, and 29/02/2002, and…)

Learning Centre, Canolfan Dysgu
Coleg Y Cymoedd, Campus Nantgarw Campus
Heol Y Coleg, Parc Nantgarw
CF15 7QY
01443 653655 / 663168

5 RISK ASSESSMENTS

Overview

What is a Risk Assessment?

A risk assessment is a vital part of everyday life. We all assess risks from the moment we get up in the morning. All that changes in our professional lives is that we have to start writing it down. Whenever we cross the road, we look both ways. We have approached a hazard, and we are now assessing the risks. We have been told about the risks through countless lectures by schools, parents and 1980's rock idols. We also have a pretty good idea how quickly we can cross the road, so our brain works out if we can make it before that rather large lorry gets here. We have just performed a risk assessment. We can get mathematical about it, work out relative speeds and distances, and even add in the extra unknown of a speeding or drunk driver, but the basic assessment stays the same.

Reviewing the Risk

As we cross the road, we tend to keep an eye out for that extra 'unknown' factor. The motorbike we didn't spot, the large patch of diesel oil in front of us... all the time we are 're-assessing' the risk. In our professional capacity, we must regularly reassess the risks, and update our original documentation. In some cases the change in circumstances is such that we must act on it immediately. In a 'professional' environment, there is as much a moral obligation as a legal one. How many of us could live with our consciences if we spotted a potentially lethal hazard, did nothing, and then had a friend seriously injured, or die, because of it. "It wasn't my job/fault/responsibility" won't cut it with your friends, even if it might in a Court of Law.

Documenting the Risk

There are three main stages to any risk assessment: Identification, Assessment, Control.

We first must identify the hazards. We must describe them sufficiently so that another, less experienced, person can recognise the hazard if confronted with it. An identification number may assist in filing and cross reference, but the description must hold up on its own.

There are many systems in place for assessing the risk with many results; some are too simple, some are too complex. In all of this, you must understand the fundamentals of the assessment. You are rating the probability that someone will die from a particular hazard. Any system that can easily be cross-referenced to a percentage scale is easiest to understand. There are three main areas that you must consider when assessing risks: seriousness of injury, frequency of the task, and the likelihood of injury should an accident happen. A secondary issue is to identify those at risk of injury, which allows the reader to determine whether they may be affected by a particular hazard.

The third part of the risk assessment is about 'controlling' the risk. What can we do to reduce the probability of death or injury.

Following the three areas described above, can we reduce the hazard from a potential death, to a survivable injury. A fall from 10 metres is more than likely going to be fatal. A fall arrest system may cause some internal injuries, or abrasions caused during a fall past equipment, but it is likely to be survivable.

Reducing the frequency of the task that exposes the hazard helps control the risk. Asking each of the departments (e.g. sound, lighting, rigging and video) on a tour to wire-in their own tails, could be four times more hazardous than getting them all done in one go, by a single, competent person.

Reducing the likelihood of injury is the third area of possible improvement. Experience and Training can be an influencing factor; so can PPE (Personal Protective Equipment). Xenon lamps are prone to explosion when handled badly. You can't reduce the frequency because they have a finite life, but the provision of gauntlet, protective jacket and visor will reduce the likelihood of injury. Clearing the stage whilst rigging is in progress isn't going to reduce the worst case injury, but it ensures that the likelihood of a dropped shackle actually hitting someone is minimal.

Not all controls can be implemented immediately. Some of them will already be in place through basic Darwinian intelligence and good working practices. It is therefore probable that some controls will end up on a 'to do' list. Most good risk assessments have a section that allows you to 'promise' to add the controls by a certain date. There will always be financial and logistical complications, but identifying the solution is more than half the problem.

Finding the Hazards

What are they? How do you find them? There are two ways to deal with this, depending which end of the food chain you are at. First you must decide if you are the best person to identify and evaluate the risks. You may be a general manager who has worked his way up through the sales team, or a production manager who used to be a lighting technician. There will always be gaps in your knowledge. If there are certain areas in which you lack experience, do as you would for all other business issues - delegate the task.

If you are at the bottom of the food chain, as always, you get the grunt work. But before you get huffy, always remember that a risk assessment is a double-edged sword. If you are charged with producing risk assessments, you must do so to the best of your ability, or the whole process is worthless. On the other hand, it is a clear way of informing management of safety issues that can be easily solved, given a little thought. By recommending controls and deadlines, you are passing the buck back to those who delegated it to you. They cannot simply file the information. As mentioned before, you cannot be delegated responsibility without authority. If you do not have the authority to implement those controls, it is up to your boss to act on your recommendations. After all, he trusted you to assess the risks in the first place...

So, you have an area to assess, where do you start? As they say, start at the beginning. Imagine your day a bit at a time, and start to identify the tasks that are performed. If you are assessing the risks of a tour, start by getting off the tour bus. For most people, unloading the trucks will be the first task, so start analysing the risks of unpacking a truck, and getting the equipment onto the stage. As you move through the day, topics such as electricity or working at heights will come up. The most important thing is to break it down into manageable chunks. Lifting a flightcase in the back of a truck will be the same as lifting it elsewhere, so don't get specific if you don't have to. On the other hand, limit each risk assessment to one type of hazard. Don't try to cover both the spill hazard and the toxic hazard of a smoke machine at the same time, or the system will become impractical.

Cutting it down to size

The worst thing you can do, as far as Health & Safety is concerned, is to have a massive project that dwindles into nothing after a few months. The whole system of risk assessments, safe working practices, controls, improvements, re-assessments... is a continual, background, task. The simplest way to spread both the effort, and the money, is to take small mouthfuls. If you run a warehouse, do a risk assessment a week. Spend ten minutes a week wandering around the warehouse, looking at things from a different angle. The simplest things will start to stand out.

By spreading the workload out in this way, it becomes a lot easier to manage. Planned right, you will have finished all the risk assessments and safe methods of work before you are due to re-assess the risks. Most people will review their risk assessments once a year. The timescale is down to you, as long as you determine the review date when you first write the assessment.

The whole underlying concept behind modern Health & Safety legislation is to allow you to determine what is safe. This has good and bad elements. The fact that you can implement your own safe working methods rather than have them imposed should allow you to tailor them to your business. The flip side is that there is less and less specific advice once you go beyond the usual.

Somewhere there will be a code of practice covering some of what you do. There are already industry specific codes covering temporary mains (BS7909), and the use of lifting equipment such as chain hoists is already well covered. By following these codes wherever possible you regain the protection of 'doing what others tell you' that used to be provided by older legislation.

Lighting

The main risks in the lighting world will be electricity and working at heights, but manual handling, COSHH and UV radiation may all have to be taken into consideration.

Sound

The main risks for sound crew will be electricity and noise, but manual handling, and safe stacking of boxes will need to be looked at.

Catering

Caterers have to deal with electricity, gas, food contamination, burns and cuts, and all sorts of other risks. We assume that the familiarity of a kitchen reduces risks, but in most cases we presume too much.

Rigging

Theoretically rigging is one of the riskier parts of our industry, working at heights, and suspending heavy loads above people's heads. However, the types of risk are limited, and as long as issues such as LOLER and PPE are properly addressed, compliance is quite simple.

Backline
The crew get off the bus at noon, have lunch and then twiddle some knobs for a couple of hours. How risky can that be? Well, once the show is under way they spend most of their time in the dark, under strict time constraints, and before they even get to the stage they have to negotiate all the cables and assorted junk the lighting and sound crew have been quietly stacking off stage since they arrived.

Security
These days, 'security' personnel are usually trained in first aid, crowd control, and even fire fighting. Their risks are as varied as any, as they usually have complete access to all areas. Warning notices and provision of proper barriers are all part of their daily life.

Staging
This is one of the riskiest parts of the industry - turning up at a green-field site when not even the toilets are working yet, and often working well into the night with inadequate lighting, in cold and wet weather (i.e most British summers). Protective clothing, manual handling, working at heights, forklifts etc are coupled with the fact that some safety officers will also expect you to conform to the 'Construction: Design & Management Regulations' (CDM) as if it were a normal building site.

Set
People building sets will be exposed to power tools, lifting and holding awkward loads, confined spaces, dust and paint fumes, and other substances I would rather not know about.

Transport
Large trucks have fairly strict regulations as far as maximum loads and driving hours. If one of your 'employees' drives a van, they may not be subject to those laws, but you still have a 'duty of care' to them. This will include ensuring that you do not expect them to do a long drive after a long day, making sure enough people are available to load and unload, that the vehicle is properly maintained and insured, and 'fit for purpose'.

On a positive note, a risk assessment may determine that your 'driving' staff would benefit from some additional training, such as advance driving courses, or half a day on a skid pan. A freelancer could have a pretty good argument with the tax man over that receipt.

Identifying the Risks

Having broken down our areas of activity into smaller chunks, we need to identify the risks. Health & Safety legislation has been split into specific areas such as electricity, manual handling, hazardous chemicals, etc. The Health & Safety Executive publish copies of the legislation accompanied by guidance, recommendations and comments.

It is important to differentiate between what is a statutory requirement (i.e. law) and what is a 'recommendation'. In the Manual Handling Operations Regulations 1992, there are no limits on how much weight a person can lift. In the guidance document, however, there are clear details of how much the average person can safety lift, based on all the research available. It is not usually the load that is the problem, but the posture.

Because the guidance is not embedded in law, it is not strictly enforceable. However, if an employee is injured lifting a 50kg box on their own, because you decided it was okay, you should have a well written risk assessment that backs up your decision! The key thing to remember is that if someone is hurt, something went wrong, and that may be a breach of the Management of Health & Safety Regulations, even if you thought you had everything covered.

A variation on the theme is an 'approved' code of practice. If you deviate from the recommendations of an Approved Code Of Practice (ACOP), you are flying in the face of (usually) superior knowledge and experience.

In the same way we have broken down hazards into areas of activity, it therefore makes sense to split it down further into types of hazard as well. It may make for more paperwork, but we are building foundations for a system that should stand forever.

Workplace Environment

This area covers the basic fabric of the work environment. It doesn't have to be a building. It covers things like the state of the floor, lighting, temperature, weather, working at heights, dropping objects from shelves, or the shelves themselves collapsing.

Manual Handling

Manual Handling covers all elements of the non-mechanically assisted (i.e. people) manoeuvring and lifting of things. Be it carrying a box of photocopier paper, or unloading a truck, you must identify every risk. Even the pushing of a flightcase is covered by these regulations.

Electricity

Electricity is covered under the Electricity At Work Regulations and can be summarised in one sweeping statement: all electrical equipment must be safe, used safely, and maintained as safe throughout its life. In practice this means regular inspections, purchasing equipment that is fit for purpose, and minimising risks not only to users (which may include performers and the public) but also to repair and maintenance staff. Live work should be avoided wherever possible (the regulations are quire clear on this), and systems must be in place to prevent the energising of equipment that is unsafe, or being worked on.

COSHH

Any chemical substance (and that includes water) has an associated risk. The Control of Substances Hazardous to Health Regulations covers all aspects of the use, handling, absorption, respiration and ingestion of these chemicals.

Every chemical product sold MUST be accompanied by a Hazard Data Sheet the first time it is sold to a client. This not only covers your suppliers, but also yourself if you pass it on (it does not even have to be sold). Any supplier who refuses to supply a data sheet is breaking the law.

The Hazard Data Sheet should cover all aspects of the chemical, what risks it poses, what first aid techniques must be used, how to clear up spills and disposal methods. Most importantly, it must cover the safe use of the chemical as well. If you are using a smoke machine, it is no good having a data sheet telling you to wash your hands after filling the machine, if neither the Hazard Data Sheet, nor the instruction manual tell you how much smoke is too much smoke, i.e. indicating maximum exposure levels.

There are also regulations covering the packaging and transportaion of chemicals that you may need to be aware of.

PUWER

The Provision and Use of Work Equipment Regulations 1998 came into force at the same time as LOLER. It covers all aspects of the 'tools' we use to perform our jobs from chisels to forklifts, from power tools to power presses.

This is a good example of the 'new style' legislation that is being brought in. It revoked a large number of individual regulations covering woodworking tools, abrasive wheels, power presses, and more and lumped them together into a much more comprehensive, and easier to understand, Statutory Instrument. The main points can be summarised as Suitability, Maintenance and Inspections, Information and Training and Competence of Users.

PPE

The Personal Protective Equipment Regulations 1992 cover the provision, use and maintenance of all equipment provided to employees to help protect them from a hazard.

In the course of doing Risk Assessments you will find that the only way to minimise some risks is by the provision of some form of PPE. Whether this is a hard hat or a harness, the employer cannot simply issue an item. It must be assessed for suitability, and inspected at regular intervals.

In the case of a self-employed person, they perform the duties of both the employer and the employee. If you are a 'true' freelancer, you cannot expect the employing company to supply you with PPE except in exceptional circumstances.

It is also worth remembering that the PPE 'Guidance on Regulations' by the HSC specifically note that "PPE should always be regarded as the last resort to protect against risks to health and safety" (Guidance note 20, ISBN 0-7176-0414-2). Therefore you should not accept the imposition of PPE by a third party (such as a venue) without seeing the relevant Risk Assessment first. PPE is like a seat belt or an air bag in a car, you never know if it is going to work until it is too late. We all know that ABS and good tyres are far more likely to save your life. We are talking about the difference between primary and secondary safety, between prevention and cure.

Fire and First Aid

Fire risks are everywhere. We are not only talking about the pile of rubbish off stage, but also about the performer who has dragged in three electric heaters into the dressing room, and plugged them all into one socket.

Fire safety is all about prevention and evacuation. Fire extinguishers are useless if they are the wrong type or the nearest person doesn't know how to use them. I have been lucky to have had the opportunity to be able to use extinguishers in real situations, had some basic training, and also let them off in the usual excesses at the end of tour party!

Assessing the risks, especially on site where you may not have access to the normal array of emergency services, can become critical. The provision of CO_2 extinguishers by the dimmer racks could stop a potential disaster. Never happen to you? It happened at Alexandra Palace, and it has happened in a large number of night-clubs, and most of us have all done gigs in one place or another which has since caught fire. I once had a very 'heated' argument with an Italian Fireman who insisted on standing by the dimmer racks (connected to 400A, 3 phase power) with a dripping fire hose. He was most offended when I told him he would die if he turned the hose on, and eventually he realised, having never seen the equipment before, what the problem was, and came back with four CO_2 extinguishers and a bottle of wine. Some arguments are worth having . . .

Make sure the emergency evacuation routes are pointed out to the crew chiefs before the cables are run. Running cables overhead is always preferable to using ramps. Ensure the crew are told how to raise an alarm properly. These things are all part of the information that a Risk Assessment should identify as necessary. If it is on site, it usually has to come from the venue, via the production manager. Knowing where the local hospital is, and what first aid facilities are available could, in a moment of panic, make all the difference.

Noise and Radiation

Noise is a factor in at least a quarter of our industry. It is not just the risk to the public, but also to our own staff. At a venue, the sound crew chief, and/or sound engineer has the potential to produce an immense amount of Sound Pressure Level. Irresponsible use of that power could cause partial deafness in someone unfortunate enough to be working out front.

All a bit of a laugh, you might say. However, standing 150 ft away, you might not know that the person is standing on the edge of the stage, and a sudden noise, or even just the sheer amount of air moved by a large bass bin array, could just push them enough to lose their balance and fall. Not so funny now, is it? Risk Assessments are all about thinking before acting and engaging brain before muscle.

Radiation may seem a strange item to have on the list, but we're not talking about nuclear reactions. We are unlikely to need to worry about small nuclear generators running our shows yet - they only build the portable ones for submarines and satellites - but the ultraviolet radiation produced by UV guns and arc light sources can do more than just give you a tan and the effects can be irreversible. And as we all know about getting sunburned - as far as UV is concerned, we are like frogs in a pan of boiling water, too stupid to notice.

Other Risks

There will always be risks that never fit into a set category. Nevertheless, they must be assessed. Strobe lighting can affect photosensitive epileptic sufferers. Then there is the use of firearms during a stunt scene plus pyrotechnics, fireworks and lasers and a plethora of equipment not yet invented.

Summary

What we have started to develop is a type of matrix. Some Risk Assessments may be only pertinent to one group, others will be the same for all. Developing a method of finding easily what applies to whom will make the documents easier to maintain and easier to issue.

6 WRITING THE RISK ASSESSMENT

Header

The header of a risk assessment should contain the following:

a   The name of the person making the assessment.

b   The date of the assessment and the 'review by' date (or the duration of validity of the assessment, e.g. the tour dates).

c   The responsible person (e.g. the department supervisor or the crew chief).

d   The premises (or venue or tour) the risk assessment refers to.

e   Any references for the show, the risk, etc that may help you maintain the system.

f   A short title describing the risk.

Risk Analysis

This section should cover a detailed description of the risk, and a quantification of the hazard enough so that someone reading it understands the hazard, and its potential for harm. The usual details entered here are:

a   Full description of the hazard. Why and how will it harm?

b   Who is at risk? Is it just your staff, or the punters as well?

c   The Severity: the worst possible outcome on an accident.

d   The Likelihood: if the risk becomes reality, how likely is it to harm someone? If a crew member drops something from the truss, how likely is it to hit someone underneath? 1 in 5? 50/50?

e   The Frequency: how often is the task that produces the risk carried out? If we are talking about wiring a set of tails into the mains, it only happens once a gig, if that.

My favourite system of quantifying risks is based on a 1 to 10 scale on each of the above. If severity 1 is a scratch not even requiring a plaster, severity 10 is death. In Likelihood, 1 is almost impossible (e.g. in the example above, the stage is cleared), 10 means it can't miss. Frequency goes from less than once a year, all the way through to continuously.

Multiply these three figures together and you get a 'per thousand' figure. Knock off a zero and you end up with a percentage figure. This gives you a stark view of the odds of your staff living to see another day. It also puts it into context. It makes it quantifiable, and that gives you a priority when looking to reduce the 'risk'. The ideal is to get as low as possible. In a real world aim to get below 10%. On some tasks you won't. But at least you now know where to spend your attention and effort. We must also identify those at risk from the Hazard. The may be passers by, of people working underneath. Only when you have assessed the full scope of the possible consequences can you start to plan the controls that will reduce the hazard to all.

Basic Content

The basic content is divided into two. First you describe what you have done to reduce the risk (you can't always affect the severity, but both the likelihood and the frequency are your's to control and manage). Some will tell you that the risk quantification should be done before these controls are introduced: some will tell you to quantify the risk after the controls are in place. Since the important thing to know is what the residual risk is, I prefer to assess all risks on the basis that all the controls are implemented. Either way, it should be clearly stated which of the two methods you are using.

The other part of the risk assessment covers what else could be done to reduce the risk further. In-house this is almost a to-do list, along with proposed completion dates. On site it could include additional controls which can only be put in place by the venue or the client. As a rigger you have no control over the permanent structure of the building, but permanently fixed and regularly tested fall-arrest anchor points would be safer than wrapping a strap around a catwalk rail.

Using the Data

Once you have gathered all this risk assessments into one place, are you done? No, sorry, it is only step one. As you produce the risk assessments with their associated controls, it is your duty to pass the information to your 'employees' (which includes contractors, sub-contractors and freelancers). In this way you start to pass on your company's work ethos. We all make a big deal about 'common sense'. Common sense is supposed to mean 'good practical wisdom especially in everyday matters'. But the real meaning of 'common' is communal. What we really need is 'communal sense'. We need to understand the risks in the same way. Simple things like 'lifting on three' versus 'lifting after three' can have serious implications when lifting a heavy box. By documenting all these little practices, and then 'publishing' them for all to read, and understand, we communise this wisdom, this experience that we all refer to as common sense. Often, these documents become 'safe working practices': a method that has been developed to reduce the risk, publicised amongst all the staff/crew...

7 SAFE WORKING PRACTICES

Overview

A Safe Working Practice, also known as a Safe System of Work, is a documented way of performing a specific job. It can be an industry code of practice, or something written within the company. Most importantly, it details a way of performing a task or duty that might otherwise be unsafe.

An obvious example would be when a distribution box needs to be powered down in order to wire in some power tails. The fuses are removed from the source, and the door locked to prevent replacement. Once the tails are fitted, the electrician unlocks the door and replaces the fuses. In the interim, only someone with a key could energise that unit, and if the keys are restricted, the end result is a safe system of work.

Safe Systems

Safe Working Practices come in all shapes. The 'No Drinks' label on a dimmer rack is a Safe Working Practice. Restricting who can power up what equipment is a Safe Working Practice.

So when we get a new person on a tour, do we bother to tell then what to do and what not to do? Usually not. We assume that the warehouse has taught them the basics, and keep a wary eye open.

But is this good enough? Not in the eyes of the Health & Safety Executive. How can we be sure that they have the same understanding, the same 'common' sense as the rest of the crew? Their inexperience may not only harm themselves, but others too.

As Safe Working Practices build up, they become a manual, a guide to the way a company does business. Add a dress code or two, and you have a detailed job description for your freelance crew, as well.

When you combine the collection of risk assessments and safe systems of work, what emerges is a method of working that is, as far as is practicable, *safe*.

8 METHOD STATEMENTS

What is usually called 'The Method Statement' is a difficult document to define. It has no proper definition in any current legislation, and therefore there can be no legal requirement for it.. Whilst the HSE refer to Method Statements in many of their documents, it is primarily used within the construction industry.

Purpose

The purpose of the Method Statement is to lay out clearly how a 'job' should be carried out. It usually relies on risk assessments and safe working practices to back it up, and the main use of the document is usually to inform other people, not directly involved in what you do, as to what hazards are involved, methods that you will be using to perform the job, and how you will ensure the safety of all involved directly or indirectly.

What to Write

The best description of what a Method Statement should contain is that it is a 'plan of work'. It should specify the location and duration of the work, the methods used (see below), type of equipment, PPE and tools being used, and how the health and safety of others (i.e. the public and other workers) is to be ensured.

Types of Equipment, etc.

What we are talking about here is access equipment such as ladders, towers, chain hoists, power tools, welding equipment, electricity, etc. The equipment we are installing can be compared to 'materials'. The equipment referred to here is work equipment.

Methods of Work

This section refers to how we will do the job. In simplest terminology it would say: "We walk in the door, unload the truck, assemble the equipment and hang it from chain hoists. The lifting operation is to be supervised by the rigger, and the connection to the house electrical supply by the dimmer man. The person in charge, the 'responsible person', is the crew chief. The stage will then be cleared. The load out will be performed in reverse order…" This doesn't really tell us a lot, but to a venue manager, it may trigger a thought process that may result in grit or salt being available for the loading dock on a cold night in winter. One lives in hope...

Protection of the Public and Other Workers

This is probably the most important part of the document. If a stage needs to be kept clear when a rigger is in the air, this is where it gets mentioned. If the sound check is going to consist of 30 minutes of extremely loud pink noise, mentioning it here may help the production manager to let everyone know to either hide, or wear ear defenders. This is no longer about you or your own staff - it is about everyone else.

Management of the Documentation

In the case of a show with a number of contractors, and a production manager in overall control, each separate party would forward a copy of their method statement and risk assessments. The production manager would then assemble all the documents into a show file, and distribute copies of the method statements to all, so that crew chiefs get a better understanding of what additional risks their teams may be exposed to, what additional personal protective equipment they may need, and in some cases, go back to the production manager to discuss a conflict of resources or locations.

9 TRAINING

Overview

There is much talk about 'training'. Some of it is good, some of it is bad. Every employer (company or self-employed) has a legal duty to ensure their staff is properly instructed in the use of the equipment and methods used during the work they are required to perform. This training can be very basic, or formal. And there is another point you have to make a decision on. The training must be appropriate to the task or equipment. It should always be documented, even if it only takes 10 minutes, and wherever possible, the training objectives should be laid out prior to a new employee joining your company or operation.

Objectives

Training objectives should be determined for every member of staff. Whether it is a plan for the office receptionist or the general manager, there will always be some simple things they need to be told. A simple objective would be to show the employee the evacuation plan, nearest fire escapes, and the assembly area. It takes one line in a training record. However, if one person dies in a fire because they didn't know how to get out, these records (if there are any left!) will be checked to see if you showed due diligence.

Apart from the legal aspects, there are also moral aspects in the planning of an employee's training. It gives them a path to follow, targets to meet, and guidance on career development.

This all sounds very 'corporate', but since most of it is already a legal requirement, it takes very little more to turn it into a valuable company tool, especially in a growing business where skills are always in short supply and often have to be found from inside the company rather than sourced from outside.

Evaluating the Training

How good is good training and how do I know whether somebody is being properly trained by their supervisors? There are two issues to quantify: is the person organising the training competent to do it, and is the person being trained understanding what he is being told?

In most industries, there is usually someone around who has been there since we all wore short trousers. Often these people been never been formally trained because there was no formal training when they started. However, you never know what they do or don't know until it is too late, and herein lies the danger. Insulting though it may be, you have to evaluate the situation and take the necessary action.

This is a management problem, and the solution will be unique to each person. In some cases they may be interested in gaining 'official' recognition of their abilities, and may simply be able to sit an examination. Others may really be into the idea of training people, and willingly agree to whatever is required. There will be those who are worried that a shortcoming, real or perceived, will become obvious and they will lose their job.

In most cases, it may be easier to get them to 'self-evaluate'. You can allow them to grade themselves, and allow others to confirm it. It's not an ideal solution, but it's simple and a starting point.

Once you have 'competent' trainers, you need to evaluate what the trainees have to learn. In some cases this can be a simple test, such as wiring up a 13Amp plug. In other cases you may wish to adopt something more formal.

However, the simplest system of all, and the most expensive, is to use a professional external source to take the necessary actions for you. Most of these will bring their own courses, some of national status, some customised to your own requirements. However, beware of those that are not ratified by a third party, such as a trade association or professional body.

10 RECORDS

Overview

Records are like expense receipts. You hang on to them in case you can use them. Records have two main uses: one internal, to allow you to trace the history of an item or person; one external, to show due diligence.

So, why do we need to keep records, and for how long? Let's start by splitting people and equipment

Personal Records

Under Health and Safety legislation you need to train people to be able to perform their jobs properly, and safely. You may have a plethora of employees, of all levels of abilities and skills. Before allowing them to perform any work for you, you must assess them. The starting point will be to find out what education, formal training and experience they have. Most people will commence their records with an application form. Do they have a forklift licence, first aid certificate, driving licence…? In some cases you may want a copy. All of these items start to build up a record.

Now we have a basic assessment of their skills, we can decide what work they are suitable for. We can draw up a matrix of jobs vs. skills. We can then draw up a matrix of employees linked to jobs. Pop it on the wall and then all the office staff know not to send Fred out as a rack man, as he has trouble wiring up a 13 Amp plug. Common sense? No - communal sense.

Equipment Records

Why do we need equipment records? To prove the equipment is safe, and has been safe for quite some time. Different equipment will come under different regulations, but the fundamentals are the same.

We regularly need to inspect, service, maintain and test most, if not all, of the equipment we use in the industry. The question is to decide as to what level and how often. Recent legislation allows you to follow the history of an item and change the level of attention based on the history.

If you have 1000 Parcans in your rental stock, and you test them every time they go out, you may end up bankrupting the company. If you already track them by serial number though a booking program, and the equipment is inspected (not tested) by competent people, you may need to do nothing more than what you are already doing. You may have to formalise things to some degree, but if you are confident that the visual and functional tests will trap the vast majority of the faults (which you would want to do anyway else you might not get paid) then that is probably sufficient.

It is not the frequency nor the complexity that matters, but the results. If your Portable Appliance Tester never finds a fault in your equipment, and you have the history to prove it, you can decide to reduce either the complexity or the frequency of the tests (or get the tester repaired!). However, you should have laid out your original test strategy in a Safe Working Practice, and now the reasons for changing that should be documented as well.

11 WHAT TO DO WHEN CHALLENGED

So we think we have done everything expected of us, covered all and every area when the venue safety officer walks towards you . . .

The first thing to remember is that most safety issues are ones of degree, and often are personal opinions and perceptions. Your informed opinion as an experienced professional can be as valid as a qualified safety inspector's.

Remember that you work day-to-day, and may have access to information that the safety officer is unaware of, and vice-versa of course. Because there are few absolutes, the main thing a good safety officer is after is confidence that you have the right approach. Most safety officers only turn up an hour or so before 'doors', and in doing so have to come to a fairly rapid opinion of the situation. Untidy cables and empty drink cans on top of the mains distro are hardly likely to set the right example.

Remember that they have a fairly thankless task. If nothing goes wrong you will grumble about what a waste of time re-running your cables over a doorway was. If a disaster happens, all fingers will point at them because "it was passed".

So the more professional your approach, the more open you are with a safety officer, the better it will be in the long term. If you have ended up running your 1000A mains run in front of an evacuation route, the fault actually lies with whoever didn't tell you about the exit, not with the safety officer, so get them to give the production manager/venue/promoter a hard time while you re-run the cables. Get the safety officer on your side.

If you end up dealing with a 'job's worth', which we have all had to do, try and work out why they are telling you to do something. If they insist on making you use the venue-supplied 30mA Residual Current Device (RCD), ask them which legislation they are referring to, show them your risk assessments for electric shock, and be prepared to stand your ground where necessary, but pick the battle areas you can, or must, win.

If a safety officer is adamant that you must change something, get it in writing. Some things may cost a lot of money to put right, and you have a right to know "what you were doing wrong". It may be as simple as a drape is no longer fireproof because someone washed it, or because it belongs to the band and it is so old it was never fireproofed in the first place. A lot could be riding on one person's opinion - so cover yourself, and your suppliers.

Be sure of your arguments. If you are a mains person, always carry a copy of the Electricity at Work regulations, and a copy of the current wiring regs (BS7671). If you are a rigger, carry a copy of LOLER, and when asked for test certificates (which you may not necessarily be legally required to show) you can counter by asking to see the test certificates for the hanging points you are using (which you are legally entitled to ask for).

12 WHEN YOU TURN UP AT A VENUE

When you first turn up at a venue, make sure you have access to all the necessary information, such as emergency numbers, phones, evacuation plans, nearest fire fighting equipment. Make a copy of the information and stick it on the side of the dimmer rack, monitor sidefills, FOH rack, etc.

Make sure you are happy with the facilities for your crew; simple things like drinking water, toilets and first aid. You have a right to these basic necessities, and if you are in a well-established venue, the management can hardly claim they didn't know about your requirements. Always remember where the money goes. If you are paying someone for a venue, or even a bit of a venue, by accepting your money, they have accepted a duty of care. You may argue with them as to the specifics, but I have heard too many stories of fire exits being locked, ambulances not being able to gain access due to locked gates, badly pot-holed loading bays, missing cable trench covers…

Too many venues ask for risk assessments and method statements without bothering to read them. It is not just a one-way street. They should be providing copies of their risk assessments to you (or at least the relevant ones) and copies of their Safety Policy. The whole point of all this documentation is not supposed to be arse-covering; it is supposed to be an exchange of information that may prevent an accident, and to help avoid confusion in the event of an emergency.

13 WHAT HAPPENS IF IT ALL GOES WRONG . . .

In the event of an accident, there are several areas that need to be addressed immediately. If necessary, they can (and perhaps should) be done by different people. First, it must be assessed whether the accident has 'finished' or whether there is still the possibility of further injury due to an unsafe structure, etc. This is very important as you also don't want to imperil the safety of those trying to help. Once the situation has been established and is stable, you must attend to those injured, which may involve first aid, or even a rescue, if a person has fallen from height and is now suspended by a fall arrester. You will also have to decide whether you need to call the emergency services. Also remember that a call on a mobile phone will often take longer to route through to the correct control room than a land line.

It is in these situations that planning organised prior to the event can become, quite literally, a life saver. If your preparatory work has been done properly, you will have avoided, for instance, the need to hunt around for the address of the nearest hospital, or the telephone number for the emergency services if you are outside the country you normally live in.

It is especially important to make sure the right people are making the right decisions, and the only way you can cover this situation is to make sure these people are on site. It is extremely important to have the knowledge of a First-Aider when trying to determine if someone is safe to move, if they are aware and responsive, and indeed, whether it is more important to rescue them than to wait for the fire brigade and ambulance services. When dealing with the rescue of someone from a height, the best person for the job is likely to be one of the riggers - even more so if one of them has first aid training.

In the aftermath of an accident, there will be more issues you have to deal with, but your priority is to deal with the situation in hand. Once the injured are in safe hands, but before the 'debris' is cleared, you need to be thinking about what happened.

There is a legal obligation to review any risk assessment "if there is reason to suspect that it is no longer valid", so you therefore need to determine the cause of the accident, and consider the elements that 'failed' in the chain of events. Remember, if there has been an accident, your system has failed in some way, and therefore you have a duty to address this issue as soon as possible. In fact, if the danger of an accident still exists, you must put temporary measures into place to prevent a recurrence of the accident.

In the event of legal action, it is not only what caused the accident that will be looked at, but how you dealt with it as well. Your actions at this point can make a huge difference to the way in which the HSE will view the case. This is why it is very important to insure that the investigation is correctly recorded as part of your paperwork.

As well as investigating the 'failure' of the system, there will probably be a legal duty to inform the relevant authorities. Under RIDDOR (the Reporting of Injuries, Diseases and Dangerous Occurrences Regulations) you have a duty to report any serious accident to your own staff and any accident involving a member of the public (in other words someone not working or someone 'passing by', including, for instance, a delegate at a conference or a member of an audience) that requires them to be taken to hospital. You also have to report certain types of 'near misses', especially if it involves a structural failure that could happen elsewhere. In the case of a death or major injury, they have to be reported "by the quickest practical means", and followed up by a written report within 10 days.

In the event of a major accident, you will probably find yourself rapidly surrounded by the police, the coroner, the Health & Safety Executive and/or the local Environment Health Officer and even your insurance company representative. There is no guarantee that they will agree on anything the others say. This can be very distressing when you have a friend or colleague lying on the floor that you cannot move until the crime scene has been recorded. I use the word 'crime', because at that point, that is what it may prove to be. Breaches of Health & Safety legislation are criminal acts.

In the multi-contractor environment we work in, it is important to ensure that someone also takes care of entries into an Accident Book. Even with a minor injury, it is very important to record the incident. If a 'victim' ever attempts to claim any compensation, this is the first place an insurance company will look. If there is no entry there is no proof an 'accident' happened at work, accident cover won't apply and compensation payments are unlikely to be made.

The first thing to note is that the HSE guidance refers to people working within "premises under the control of someone else", and it is that "someone else" who is responsible for reporting and recording any accidents, injuries, diseases and/or dangerous occurrences.

It is therefore very important to determine who is in control of the premises. Is it the venue management, or the event production manager? This is an issue that needs to be determined before arriving at a venue or location.

Either way, I would recommend that the production manager of any event keeps a log of accidents for use by all the event staff. This should be filed back in the office on an event-by-event basis, and kept for the required minimum of three years.

In the aftermath of an accident, there will be the inevitable blame shifting, finger pointing and long discussions with insurance companies. No matter where you were in the chain of events, it is vital you have insurance cover for the work you do. If you are self-employed, you cannot and must not assume that someone else's insurance will cover you, because their insurance company will try and disown you no matter what. Also, if you are self-employed, you can find youself in a very unprotected situation. A limited company has, by its very name, limited liability, and must, by law, have public and employers' insurance. The correct form of insurance is even more important for a freelancer who may have a home or other assets that could be seized and sold to pay any resultant claim.

If your actions - or lack of action - was seen to have caused an accident you can be held liable, and nobody else's insurance will cover you. Don't make the mistake of thinking that your 'employer' covers you. They don't! Even if they have additional cover, it is usually to protect themselves from you and not the other way round. A self-employed freelancer without public liability insurance is either a very stupid person, or someone who really ought to be paid on a PAYE basis and therefore covered as an employee. If you are taxed under what most people call 'Schedule D', you **need** public liability insurance.

Under the Employer's Liability (Compulsory Insurance) Regulations, every employer is required to have a minimum of public and employers liability insurance. There is no reference to self-employed people in this document, but neither are they specifically excluded. I am therefore of the opinion that as your own employer, you **must** have public and employee liability insurance, **and** you must be able to produce proof of cover when asked by an inspector, and to keep that proof for 40 years (Scanned copies of mine are on my web site, for anyone to see).

A1 APPLICABLE REGULATIONS

The Employers 'Six Pack'

Management of Health and Safety at Work Regulations

The main points in this legislation are to do with the responsibilities of managers (not just the company, but each and every manager, supervisor and self employed person) to their staff, directly employed or not.

The Statutory Instrument (i.e. the law) lays out the requirement for carrying out risk assessments (documented or otherwise, although the law says the company needs five employees or more before they have to be documented, the risk assessments still need to be done), undertaking and reviewing preventative and protective measures, health surveillance (which isn't just eye tests, but also ensuring your crew aren't so tired they fall asleep at the wheel on the way home), informing and instructing employees in the risks and the protective measures, and the obligation on each and every one to co-ordinate and co-operate with other employers and self-employed persons in a multi-employer environment.

Manual Handling Operations Regulations

These regulations cover anything to do with "transporting or supporting a load (including the lifting, putting down, pushing, pulling, carrying or moving thereof) by hand or bodily force". The aim is given that about a third of all reported injuries in the workplace are due to the result of incorrect lifting (and dropping) of manual loads, this came in with quite a bang. The aim is to reduce the risk to health by encouraging the use of mechanical assistance, better posture and better ergonomic planning of the workplace.

The regulations themselves are very short and to the point, and the HSE guidance is a mine of knowledge on the 'average' lifting capability, safe methods of lifting, and all sorts of useful information.

The HSE also make specific reference to poorly lit areas and uneven floors. Sounds like every gig I've ever been to . . .

Electricity at Work Regulations (EAW)

These regulations cover any electrical system, of any age, low voltage, high tension, 12v; anything electrical at all and no exceptions. None. Even your Mag-Lite, and especially your illegally imported cattle prod, which has proved so useful in getting the crew out of the tour bus or hotel in the morning.

These are one of the few regulations where there are ABSOLUTE duties and that means the usual 'as far as is practicable' doesn't cut it.

In a nutshell, all electrical systems must be designed to prevent danger, maintained to prevent danger, and be operated in a way to prevent danger... These regulations are law, the Wiring Regulations are only a Standard.

If you design, build, operate or maintain electrical equipment within your company or as part of your work duties, this is the ultimate document. Before ever getting into an argument about electricity, read this document first. This is the document to quote when you want to shut down the lighting rig due to 'unsuitable weather conditions' (regulation 6).

These are serious regulations. There aren't the usual exclusions for the armed forces, and apart from ships, aircraft and hovercraft, (whose captain is ultimately responsible already), the only exclusions are if the HSE give you one in writing.

PAT (Portable Appliance Testing): As a side issue, a lot of people refer to the 'PAT regulations'. There is no such thing. The regulation that covers PAT is the Electricity at Work regulation 4(2), which is the duty to "maintain the equipment to prevent danger". There are other references to maintenance in other legislation, including the Health & Safety Act and the Management of Health & Safety at Work regulations.

There is a duty to lay out an inspection and maintenance plan, and to record the findings; the rest has been made up by people like the IEE and the PAT equipment manufacturers.

Personal Protective Equipment Regulations

The PPE regulations cover all those items that protect you from danger; your climbing harness, your ear plugs, even your work clothes.

The HSE constantly remind us that PPE is a 'last resort'. ALL other measures should have been taken before you have to use PPE. My favourite argument is the hard hat. A lot of venues have a hard hat policy, but few of them will take the time to explain to you why. In an industry that is used to people working above you, the emphasis has always been on the people above not having things to drop, emptying pockets, tools on lanyards, etc, i.e. prevention rather than cure.

There is a duty to regularly inspect and maintain PPE by the employer. For those of you who are self-employed, this means *you*. If you expect the company you are working for to provide PPE, you are telling them that you are an employee and should be taxed as PAYE. For companies who provide 'pools' of PPE, such as ear defenders and hard hats, remember personal hygiene. It may be cheaper in the long run to individually issue the items than have them cleaned every time they are used.

Regular inspection should be carried out of any PPE in accordance with the manufacturers instructions. For some items you may not have the expertise in house to carry out the work, and in some cases you may find it cheaper (or easier) to use disposable items.

VDU Regulations

The Health and Safety (Display Screen Equipment) Regulations cover any use of computers and terminals. They allow you to distinguish between regular and occasional users, and the main issues covered and preventing eye strain and associated headaches, and Repetitive Strain Injury. Regular breaks, properly laid out keyboards and monitors, and avoiding screen reflections take care of most of the requirements of the regulations. They are primarily aimed at data entry staff, and people like graphic and CAD operators.

Workplace

These regulations cover everything that a building needs, from toilets to lighting, access routes to stacking, heating and rest facilities. They cover the basic necessities that an employer is legally bound to provide.

Although of most interest to employers with premises, it is a useful tool in an argument about what should be provided on-site by who, and I would recommend that all production managers should read it, and add a clause about it into contracts with promoters and venues.

Hazardous Substances & Chemicals

Control Of Substances Hazardous to Health

The COSHH regulations cover any chemicals that could present a hazard.

All manufacturers must create a data sheet explaining the risks, the precautions, storage information and the main chemicals used. This is law, and should cover usage as well (smoke machine manufacturers please note).

All chemicals that are used must be the subject of a risk assessment. Even if it is the same chemical by a different manufacturer, it must be assessed separately and precautions drawn up and followed.

Please note there are also regulations covering the transportation and packaging of chemicals which may apply to your trucking company. You should always inform them of any chemicals you are carrying with you.

Gas

The are special regulations covering the use of gas appliances, which include the duties of a landlord to regularly check central heating boilers, etc. Remember that if your catering company uses gas appliances, you will need to check ventilation and storage arrangements, and you may need to ask the supplier for copies of maintenance reports.

Pressure Vessels

There are regulations covering any item that may hold liquids (or gases) under pressure. This would cover an air compressor with a storage tank, but not necessarily a Hydrovane type. Pressure vessels and associated items (hoses, couplings, etc) must be regularly checked.

Machinery

Lifting Operations and Lifting Equipment Regulations

LOLER first came into force in late 1998. None of it was that new, it just pulled together a lot of individual elements into one set of new regulations.

It covers any item used for lifting, including accessories, and how a lifting operation should be planned and carried out. Equipment must be regularly inspected (although the timescale is not specified), and must show the safe working load on it, even if it is just a shackle.

There are arguments about whether a carabiner is a piece of lifting equipment or PPE. The answer depends on what you use it for. Either way, both regulations require the equipment to have regular inspections, so what's the point of an argument...

Provision and Use of Work Equipment Regulations

This was revised in conjunction with LOLER in 1998, and covers all equipment used by employees, from a screwdriver to a forklift truck.

It replaces many smaller regulations, such as the Abrasive Wheels regulations, and many work-working specific regulations, into a much simpler set. Like so many of the newer regulations, equipment must be safe, fit for purpose, and the staff correctly trained and instructed in its use.

In practice this means anything from throwing away broken screwdrivers to stop someone doing something stupid with it, to ensure the guards work (and are being used) on a pillar drill.

Accidents and emergencies
First Aid
Every employer has a duty to make provisions for first aid. It is not enough to assume that the ambulance crew can pick up the pieces of your accident.

This duty may involve getting staff trained either as appointed persons, or qualified first-aiders, and every production manager should ensure they have adequate cover not just for show time, but for the build period as well.

You may also have to supply a first aid kit, and ensure it is properly stocked, and not abused.

RIDDOR
The Reporting of Injuries, Diseases and Dangerous Occurrances Regulations require you to have an accident book, and to call the HSE immediately in the event of a major tragedy. These responsibilities can get vague in a gig situation, with contractors, sub contractors, freelancers, promoters, performers and the public all running about.

Less known is the fact that near misses may be reportable as well. The accident happened, and the HSE will want to know why something failed. Remember that if something structural failed in normal use, many other people may be affected, and the prompt issue of an enforcement or improvement notice could save someone's life.

Fire
There are a number of regulations covering fire. Some are specific to venues and sport grounds, some are specific to highly flammable chemicals, which include some types of paint and oil, as well as regulations covering explosives (i.e. pyrotechnics and fireworks).

The basics cover emergency exits and signs, storage, tidiness, fire fighting equipment, and emergency procedures. If you are in a venue, you should always know where the emergency exits are, the nearest fire alarm point (or procedure) and the nearest fire extinguisher of the right type.

Other

Radiation

Let's hope we have a way to go before the diesel generator gets replaced by a small Fast Breeder reactor (although General Electric have recently launched a 24MW beast based on four trailers and a jet engine, so maybe the idea isn't so far fetched). Radiation isn't just produced by nuclear devices. UV guns can produce nasty skin burns, and can lead to permanent eye damage. UV is not just produced by UV tubes and guns, but also by arc sources such as HTI and Xenon.

Infrared is also a source of radiation, and burns (and therefore fires) can be produced by a light beam from some of the more powerful spot luminaires.

Noise

Noise is a subject that any sound engineer has to deal with. There are certain specific levels that in a factory environment, would require automatic use of ear protection, but we have all seen punters stick their heads inside bass bins. More and more, local safety officers are monitoring sound levels, and automatic shutdown equipment is operable in many venues.

One thing to remember is that the PA is not the only source of noise; 10,000 kids can scream very loudly, and having your power shut off just as the band walk on stage is not going to do your blood pressure much good.

We are also not just talking about maximum levels, but also relative levels. When trying to move a truss, if you can't hear someone who is helping to watch the lift, you should ask the person making the noise to cease for a while. It only takes about two minutes to get a truss to trim height.

Working Time Directive

Under recently introduced law, employees have a right to a maximum number of work hours per week (48). This time is averaged over a 17-week period, and there are certain exemptions, like the police, and of course, junior doctors (after all, why should their lack of sleep affect your safety...?).

An employer can negotiate with its employees for a voluntary agreement to work longer hours, but this should be agreed in writing, and subject to regular review or renewal.

There are also statutory rest periods: in-work breaks (20 minutes uninterrupted in the middle of the day), a daily rest of 11 consecutive hours between each working day, and a weekly rest period of not less than 24 hours in each 7 day period (may be averaged over 2 weeks), and special considerations for 'night workers' (3+ hours of night work per day).

Freelancers are also excluded from these regulations but production managers must note that if you change the 'terms of agreement' between yourself and a freelancer during the course of a project, and then apply undue pressure to make them work additional hours without re-negotiation, you may leave yourself open to legal and civil action.

A2 EXAMPLES AND SAMPLES

The following pages contain a variety of examples and samples of documentation you will either have to write, or read, in your professional capacity. They are based on a fictitious show, and a fictitious band, production company and crew.

These documents do not form a full set, and are only provided as guidance on what the documentation looks like, and a selection of hazards you may face. Hopefully, in conjunction with the main text of this book, they will help you to understand better what the basic requirements of health and safety documentation are.

There is no benefit gained by simply churning out paperwork, and undoubtedly it is the most tedious part of health and safety, but it is also key to the spreading of information throughout a complex arrangement of clients, promoters, performers, production managers and crew.

The Cast:
The Band: Threshold Of Pain
The Show: 19th Comeback Tour
The Venue: The Royston Hippodrome
The Band's Company: Bleeding Ears Ltd.
The Production Manager: Kay Nyne
The Production Company: Headless Chicken Productions Ltd.
The Managing Director: Mack Evellian
The Account Handler: Lee Aison
The Crew Chief : Dee Riggs
The First Aider: Howard Eino

ON-SITE HEALTH AND SAFETY POLICY:

The Royston Hippodrome
Valid from: 1st January, 2001
Valid to: 31st December, 2001

Headless Chick Productions
Tel: 00 1 234 567 8900
Fax: 00 1 234 567 8911

1. Statement of Policy

Our policy is to provide and maintain safe and healthy working conditions, equipment, and systems of work for all our employees, and to provide such information, training and supervision as they need for this purpose. We also accept our responsibility for the health and safety of other people who may be affected by our activities.

The allocation for duties for safety matters and the particular arrangements which we will make to implement the policy are set out in this document.

The policy will be kept up to date, as new legislation is introduced, as new equipment is acquired by the company, and as the facilities and technology within the industry make safer systems of work possible. To ensure this, the policy and the way in which it has operated will be reviewed every year.

Signed & Dated:

✓   Mack Evellian (Managing Director)

2. Responsibilities

2.0.1.   Overall and Final responsibility (Company Wide)
Overall and final responsibility for health and safety within the company resides with:

✓ Mack Evellian (Managing Director)

2.0.1.   Overall and Final responsibility (On-Site)
When "On-Site", the person with overall and final responsibility for Health and Safety resides with:

✓ Kay Nyne (Production Manager)
2.0.1.   Day to Day (On Site)

When working "On-Site", the responsibility for the health and safety of the company's employees and sub-contractors (aka Freelancers) resides with:

✓ Dee Riggs (Crew Chief)

2.1. Employees & Sub Contractors (aka Freelancers)

All employees and sub-contractors (aka Freelancers) have the responsibility to co-operate with supervisors and managers to achieve a healthy and safe workplace and to take reasonable care of themselves and others.

It is considered part of the work duties that any employee or sub-contractor who becomes, or is made aware of a safety issue, should immediately act on that information.

All Sub-Contractors are expected to supply (and maintain) their own PPE as required by the normal and expected day to day work requirements. These would normally include (but not be limited to) Safety Harness and fall arrest equipment, Protective headwear and footwear. Ear protection (such as ear plugs) and gloves for equipment handling.

2.2. On Site disagreements

There will always be situations where differing opinions and experiences lead to a disagreement about a safety aspect of an event. The crew will endeavour to avoid any situation where this becomes a problem, however, it may be necessary, especially in the event of potential expenditure, for the Crew Chief to obtain instruction in writing from the safety inspector, prior to proceeding with the requested or required modifications and changes.

In the unlikely event that the local safety officer's request is later found to be unsubstantiated, or worse, dangerous, the company and it's staff can therefore protect itself from a decision that was forced upon it.

2.3. Consultation

Due to the small size of the company and its reliance on sub-contractors, no formal consultation system has been set up for on-site work. However, all employees and sub-contractors are involved with identifying and minimising risks on a daily basis, and are encouraged to actively partake in the setting up and revision of safe systems of work.

3. General Arrangements

3.1. On-Site Work

The nature of the company's business involves on site work. The nature of on-site work cannot easily be determined in advance. All staff required to work (or visit) "On-Site" operations should be made aware of all commonly found risks, and should contact the "On-Site" crew chief, or the event Production Manager prior to starting work.

The company will provide, when crew are being provided as part of the rental agreement, an "On-Site" safety box, which will include any necessary PPE, risk assessments for the event, and appropriate work instructions.

Safe systems of work are continuously being developed, and the company will provide, in the "On-Site" safety box, a regularly updated set of instructions. It will be the employee's (and sub-contractor's) duty to check to see if any new instructions have been added.

3.2. Accidents

3.2.1. First Aid Boxes

The "On-Site" safety box includes a small first aid kit. The seal on this is checked before each job. In addition to this, Kay Nyne (Production Manager) and The Royston Hippodrome staff should also have access to First Aid facilities.

3.2.2. Appointed persons & First Aiders

The appointed person / First Aider while "On Site" is:

✓ Howard Eino (First Aider)

3.2.3. Accident Book

An Accident Book is kept in the "On-Site" safety box. This should be used as a temporary method of recording details of accidents and emergencies until the information can be transferred to the main company accident book. RIDDOR forms are included in the On-Site safety box. These should be used in the event of a major accident.

The person responsible for maintaining the "On-Site" Accident Book and the reporting of incidents is:

✓ Kay Nyne (Production Manager)

3.3. Fire Safety

3.3.1. Escape Routes
It is the duty of the Production Manager / Venue to ensure that all crew are made aware of all the applicable escape routes, not only for their own use, but to prevent them from being blocked during the event.

✓ Kay Nyne (Production Manager)
✓ The Venue Safety Officer

3.3.1. Fire Fighting Equipment
It is the duty of the Production Manager / Venue to ensure that the correct type of fire fighting equipment is made available to the crew.

✓ Kay Nyne (Production Manager)
✓ The Venue Safety Officer

3.3.1. Raising the Alarm
It is the duty of the Production Manager / Venue to ensure that the crew are made aware of the correct way of raising the alarm, and how to react during an incident.

✓ Kay Nyne (Production Manager)
✓ The Venue Safety Officer

4. Hazards
4.1. Location of Information
The On-Site risk assessments carried out by the company are passed on to the Production manager of the Event, where they should be made available to any crew person. Additional copies will be kept in the main office, and also in the On-Site Safety box.

Manufacturers information, and Safe Systems of Work will be included in the same safety box, together with the appropriate risk assessment

4.2. Housekeeping and Premises

4.2.1.   Cleanliness
It is considered part of every employees and sub-contractors duties to maintain as clean a work environment as possible. Casual disregard of consumables, empty food and drink containers, etc is not acceptable. Apart from the fire risk and trip hazards such untidiness can present, it may also create additional, unforeseen, dangers during the load out.

4.2.2.   Waste Disposal
The Crew chief show ensure that any consumables that require special disposal, (such as smoke machine oil, spray cans and aerosols, solvent cleaner) are correctly disposed of. This may simply require a quick check with the Production Manager or the venue management as to their own arrangements.

4.2.3.   Safe Stacking and Storage
Any equipment and empty flightcases should be stored in such a way as to be stacked securely, and not present a danger to other members of the crew. This also includes ensuring that access and egress routes are kept clear.

4.2.4.   Gangways
Where access is needed to escape routes, or clear throughways to other parts of the venue, gangways will be should be clearly marked. Before running cables, the crew chief should check as to the preferred methods of crossing such routes (whether by ramps, tape or running overhead). Where temporary routes are created (such as on stage) they should be clearly marked with tape, and any trip hazards removed or clearly identified.
In addition, it may be necessary to add additional lighting for certain parts of the route, and if necessary, have battery backup.

4.3. Manual Handling
All Rental Equipment is stored and travelled in purpose build flightcases.
All flightcases are clearly marked with the weight of the case (including

contents).

The flightcases are designed to travel safely inside a van or truck, but require the use of load straps or bars to secure the load.

It is advisable, when a client provides transport, to ensure that they provide a ramp or tail lift to assist the unloading at either end.

4.4. Personal Protective Equipment (PPE)

All Full Time Staff are provided with any PPE that may be required on site (as identified by the company's risk assessments). Sub-Contracted staff (Free-lancers) are expected to provide (and maintain) their own (within reason).

When the company provides crew as well as equipment (aka "wet hire") the event will be provided with a (or a number of) "On-Site" safety boxes, which will include any additional PPE required on site.

Any additional PPE required on site by the client must be communicated to the company prior to the event, and may incur an additional charge if the company was unaware of this requirement prior to the acceptance of the order.

4.5. Electrical Equipment (EAW)

4.5.1.   Rental Inventory

All rental inventory receives a formal visual inspection prior to leaving the warehouse on a job. This involves a full check of all cabling, and accessories, and a full power up functional test.

All rental inventory is fully tested at least once a year.

4.5.2.   Live Work

As little live work as possible is carried out by the staff. However, occasionally this is unavoidable due to the need to test repairs, or equipment returned form dry hire in an unknown state. As well as performing visual checks, RCD protection is provided wherever live work is likely to be required.

4.6. LOLER

4.6.1.   Lifting Equipment

All rental inventory receives a visual inspection prior to leaving the warehouse on a job. The equipment is also formally inspected at least once a year.

The test reports are kept in the main office and are usually only provided on demand.

4.6.2. Lifting Operations

The company normally employs professional rigging companies to carry out lifting operations. Where this is not possible, the company will directly employ a competent professional to perform the "responsible person" duties under LOLER. This includes directing any lifting operation, as well as final safety checks prior to the first lift after assembly.

4.7. Machinery (PUWER)

All power tools used by the company's staff are regularly inspected, and where necessary, any maintenance logged.

Any use of plant (e.g. Fork Lift Trucks) will be restricted to properly trained staff. While "On Site" it is the responsibility of Dee Riggs (Crew Chief) to ensure that any Plant equipment is used properly and not abused in any way. It will be the responsibility of Mack Eyellian (Managing Director) to ensure that the training records are kept up to date.

4.8. Dangerous Substances (COSHH)

Few dangerous substances are used by the company. These are restricted to cleaning fluids, the occasional use of paint, and some special effects. These chemicals are rarely used on site. Full information is contained with the risk assessments

4.9. Work Stations (VDU)

There is some 'On-Site" use of workstation equipment, but all operating staff are aware of the need to have regular breaks, and are usually able to set up the equipment to their own requirements.

4.10. Fluids under Pressure

The company possesses small mobile air compressors which are used for smoke & mist effects. Full information is contained with the risk assessment.

4.11.　Other Important Hazards

The nature of working of "On-Site" is such that a number of unforeseen hazards can occur due to the large number of different groups of people. Many of these risks, though uncommon to the normal duties of the staff, have been documented in the risk assessments. As they are uncommon, they do not present a major risk, but staff must be familiar with them in order to be able to recognise them.

When "On-Site" it is the duty of the person with overall responsibility (Kay Nyne (Production Manager)) to inform any all the staff of all the identified risks they may encounter. It is our experience that this important feedback path can fail, therefore company provides as much coverage within the risk assessments as is practicable.

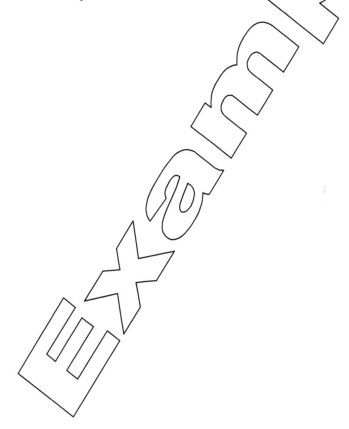

Risk Levels (Average Event duration - 5 days)

	Severity What is the worst outcome?	Likelihood If it happens how likely is it to injure?	Frequency How often is the task carried out?
1	Minor injury not requiring treatment	Almost impossible	Once every fifty Events
2	Minor injury requiring treatment not resulting in absence	Very unlikely	Once every ten Events
3	Minor injury resulting in less than 3 days absence	Unlikely	Once every five Events
4	Injury resulting in 3 days to 3 weeks absence	Fairly unlikely	Every other Event
5	Over 3 weeks absence with eventual full recovery	Even chance	Once every Event
6	Over 3 weeks absence with eventual partial recovery	Good chance	Twice every Event
7	Serious injury resulting in permanent slight disability	Probable	Once a day
8	Serious injury resulting in permanent partial disability	Very likely	Twice a day
9	Serious injury resulting in permanent severe disability	Almost inevitable	Five times a day
10	Fatality	Inevitable	Ten times a day

The three resulting numbers are multiplied together to give a risk factor with a maximum result of 1000. Because the whole system is based on a base of ten, it is much easier to convert to a percentage figure i.e. 125 = 12.5%

Risk Factor

1 to 99 (0% - 10%)	Minor risks (or substantial risks properly controlled). Even a 10% risk is still a one in ten chance of something going wrong, so this does not mean we should be complacent
100 to 199 (10% - 20%)	Medium risks: Need careful monitoring to ensure existing precautions are followed, and a long term view to decreasing the risk wherever possible
200 to 499 (20% - 50%)	Major risks that need urgent attention. The task that is being performed, or the conditions under which is being done needs to be re-considered.
Above 500 (50% - 100%)	The mathematical probability of injury or death is such that theoretically one of the company's employees will be dead or badly hurt by the end of the day.

Production:	"Threshold of Pain" World Tour
Venue:	The Royston Hippodrome
Date/s of Show:	29th February, 2001
Client:	Bleeding Ears Ltd.
HCP Contact:	Lee Aison
Job Reference #:	546372/2000

Risk Assessment:	HCP 1
Area / Activity:	Truck loading and unloading
Type of Risk:	Manual Handling

Description of Risk: Heavy Cases

Equipment is supplied in cases and/or dollies which have to be unloaded from truck prior to start of load-in. Some boxes are stacked, most are heavy, and all require care and attention.

Persons at risk: HEADLESS Crew, Venue crew and truck driver

Level of risk after implementation of existing controls

Severity (1 to 10)	4
Likelihood (1 to 10)	3
Frequency (1 to 10)	5
Risk Rating (max 1000)	60 - Minor risk

Existing Controls (provided by Headless Chicken Productions Ltd.)

All trucks are loaded with care prior to despatch.
All HEADLESS Crew are familiar with weight of contents of flightcases.
All HEADLESS Crew are familiar with manual handling techniques.

Additional Controls (to be provided by Client / Venue)

A minimum of 4 crew (combined HEADLESS/Venue) should be available to unload or pack and truck requiring lifting of tipping.
A HEADLESS department crew member should always be requested to be available during truck loading and unloading.
A level truck area should be provided wherever practical.

HEADLESS on Site representative: **Dee Riggs**

Production:	"Threshold of Pain" World Tour
Venue:	The Royston Hippodrome
Date/s of Show:	29th February, 2001
Client:	Bleeding Ears Ltd.
HCP Contact:	Lee Aison
Job Reference #:	546372/2000
Risk Assessment:	HCP 2
Area / Activity:	Special Effects
Type of Risk:	Fire and First Aid

Description of Risk: **Burns caused by Dry Ice**

We may use "Dry Ice" as an effect. The handling of dry ice, due to it's low temperature, and violent reaction to produce the effect, can produce skin burns.

Persons at risk: HEADLESS Crew, Venue Crew

Level of risk after implementation of existing controls

Severity (1 to 10)	6
Likelihood (1 to 10)	3
Frequency (1 to 10)	5
Risk Rating (max 1000)	90 Low Risk

Existing Controls (provided by Headless Chicken Productions Ltd.)

All modern Dry Ice machines are fully enclosed to minimise slashes and spills.

All crew involved with loading the machine wear protective clothing, goggles and gloves, and follow the manufacturer's recommended loading procedure.

Additional Controls (to be provided by Client / Venue)

All Venue supplied staff should be made aware of the risks of handling Dry Ice without adequate protection.

HEADLESS on Site representative: **Dee Riggs**

Production:	"Threshold of Pain" World Tour
Venue:	The Royston Hippodrome
Date/s of Show:	29th February, 2001
Client:	Bleeding Ears Ltd.
HCP Contact:	Lee Aison
Job Reference #:	546372/2000
Risk Assessment:	HCP 3
Area / Activity:	General
Type of Risk:	Workplace Safety

Description of Risk: Access to and from stage/Trips and falls

Access from the stage to all other areas must be safe from trip hazards, as well as avoiding slip hazards on any ramps or stairs.

Persons at risk:	All Crew, clients, performers and members of the public.

Level of risk after implementation of existing controls

Severity (1 to 10)	3
Likelihood (1 to 10)	4
Frequency (1 to 10)	10
Risk Rating (max 1000)	120 - Medium Risk - Needs monitoring

Existing Controls (provided by Headless Chicken Productions Ltd.)

HEADLESS crew will keep access routes clear by running cables overhead & out of reach (~2.5m), or by using cable ramps. If the route is not a fire escape route, smaller cables can be covered with gaffer or hazard tape (as appropriate).

Additional Controls (to be provided by Client / Venue)

Venue should provide an area for the storage of empty flightcases. Venue should advise HEADLESS Crew as to which routes are classified as evacuation routes.
Acceptable cable routes to control, camera and followspot positions should be negotiated prior to the running of the cable.

HEADLESS on Site representative: Dee Riggs

Production:	"Threshold of Pain" World Tour
Venue:	The Royston Hippodrome
Date/s of Show:	29th February, 2001
Client:	Bleeding Ears Ltd.
HCP Contact:	Lee Aison
Job Reference #:	546372/2000
Risk Assessment:	HCP 4
Area / Activity:	Rigging
Type of Risk:	Lifting Equipment and Lifting Operations

Description of Risk: **Danger from falling objects**

Equipment used is suspended from trusses and pipes which is either hung from chain hoists attached to roof beams, or by a ground support system.

| Persons at risk: | All crew, clients, performers, members of the public |

Level of risk after implementation of existing controls

Severity (1 to 10)	10
Likelihood (1 to 10)	1
Frequency (1 to 10)	10
Risk Rating (max 1000)	100 - Medium risk - needs monitoring

Existing Controls (provided by Headless Chicken Productions Ltd.)

All hoists and motors provided by HEADLESS are regularly tested.

All rigging work is done by experienced and competent crew

All secondary equipment attached to the supporting structure has at least two points of attachment, a hook and a safety bond.

All weight measurements and allowances are based on test data supplied by manufacturers.

Additional Controls (to be provided by Client / Venue)

Details of any non HEADLESS equipment to be attached to the truss should be provided prior to the event.

Details of roof loading and SWL of points should be provided by the venue prior to the event (for details see LOLER 1998).

HEADLESS on Site representative: **Dee Riggs**

Production:	**"Threshold of Pain" World Tour**
Venue:	**The Royston Hippodrome**
Date/s of Show:	**29th February, 2001**
Client:	**Bleeding Ears Ltd.**
HCP Contact:	**Lee Aison**
Job Reference #:	**546372/2000**
Risk Assessment:	**HCP 5**
Area / Activity:	Overhead Work
Type of Risk:	Fire and First Aid

Description of Risk: Danger from falling objects
Persons under personnel working above are at danger from objects being dropped.

Persons at risk: HEADLESS Crew, Venue crew, other crew

Level of risk after implementation of existing controls

Severity (1 to 10)	10
Likelihood (1 to 10)	2
Frequency (1 to 10)	6
Risk Rating (max 1000)	120 - Medium risk - Needs monitoring

Existing Controls (provided by Headless Chicken Productions Ltd.)
HEADLESS Crew use harnesses whilst working on trusses at trim height and are trained in ropework skills.
Access equipment is visually inspected for defects before use.
HEADLESS Crew are required to empty pockets of any items that may fall out, and all tools will be attached via safety lanyards.
All equipment hung from trusses use a secondary safety bond.

Additional Controls (to be provided by Client / Venue)
Hard hat controls for other personnel working in affected areas.
Any additional non-HEADLESS crew requiring access to the truss must have a suitable harness.

HEADLESS on Site representative: Dee Riggs

Production:	"Threshold of Pain" World Tour
Venue:	The Royston Hippodrome
Date/s of Show:	29th February, 2001
Client:	Bleeding Ears Ltd.
HCP Contact:	Lee Aison
Job Reference #:	546372/2000
Risk Assessment:	HCP 6
Area / Activity:	General
Type of Risk:	Electricity at Work

Description of Risk: Risk of Electric shock

During the load-in and load-out, care must be taken to prevent equipment being damaged, circuits being powered up by mistake and incorrect connection of circuits and conductors.

| Persons at risk: | HEADLESS Crew |

Level of risk after implementation of existing controls

Severity (1 to 10)	10
Likelihood (1 to 10)	3
Frequency (1 to 10)	5
Risk Rating (max 1000)	150 - Medium risk - Needs monitoring

Existing Controls (provided by Headless Chicken Productions Ltd.)

The HEADLESS Crew Chief will nominate a member of the crew as "Mains person", who will be the only person on the HEADLESS crew to make final connections and power up the system. On a large production the system may be physically and electrically split, which may require more than one "mains" person. All devices, connectors and cables will be clearly identified to avoid misconnections. Multicores are used wherever possible to reduce risk.

Additional Controls (to be provided by Client / Venue)

Connections into permanent venue or generator power should be carried out by a competent "house" or generator company electrician who understands three phase high current applications.
Other crew should be instructed never to connect anything into the HEADLESS electrical system without the "mains" person's permission

HEADLESS on Site representative: **Dee Riggs**

Production:	**"Threshold of Pain" World Tour**
Venue:	**The Royston Hippodrome**
Date/s of Show:	**29th February, 2001**
Client:	**Bleeding Ears Ltd.**
HCP Contact:	**Lee Aison**
Job Reference #:	**546372/2000**
Risk Assessment:	**HCP 7**
Area / Activity:	Emergency Procedures
Type of Risk:	Fire and First Aid

Description of Risk: **Safe evacuation**

In any publicly attended event, fire precautions are paramount, as are ensuring that all evacuation routes are clear.

Persons at risk: Everybody

Level of risk after implementation of existing controls

Severity (1 to 10)	10
Likelihood (1 to 10)	2
Frequency (1 to 10)	10
Risk Rating (max 1000)	200 - Major risk - See additional controls

Existing Controls (provided by Headless Chicken Productions Ltd.)

HEADLESS Crew will (if made aware) avoid running cables across fire exit routes.

All HEADLESS drapes. Scrims, etc are of a fire retardant type.

All HEADLESS Crew will adhere to any publicised "No Smoking" areas

Additional Controls (to be provided by Client / Venue)

The correct types of fire fighting equipment should be provided at the primary HEADLESS crewing points (i.e. Dimmers, FOH...)

All Personnel should be informed of the venue's fire procedures and routes, including warning messages (Electrical systems are safer powered down)

HEADLESS on Site representative: **Dee Riggs**

Production:	"Threshold of Pain" World Tour
Venue:	The Royston Hippodrome
Date/s of Show:	29th February, 2001
Client:	Bleeding Ears Ltd.
HCP Contact:	Lee Aison
Job Reference #:	546372/2000
Risk Assessment:	HCP 1
Area / Activity:	Sound
Type of Risk:	Noise

Description of Risk: Temporary or permanent loss of hearing

Sound systems at live events are capable of producing sound pressure levels that could lead to temporary or permanent loss of hearing.

Persons at risk: All Crew, Members of the Public

Level of risk after implementation of existing controls

Severity (1 to 10)	7
Likelihood (1 to 10)	2
Frequency (1 to 10)	6
Risk Rating (max 1000)	84 - Minor risk

Existing Controls (provided by Headless Chicken Productions Ltd.)

All HEADLESS Crew have access to ear plugs. Ear defenders will be supplied when necessary.

HEADLESS operated sound systems will comply with noise restrictions imposed by local authorities (If made aware of them).

Multiple warnings will be issued to crew before any continuous, high level use of sound system, such as pink noise or sound checks.

Additional Controls (to be provided by Client / Venue)

Client or Venue provided sound system should comply with noise restrictions imposed by local authorities.

Multiple warnings should be issued to crew before any continuous, high level use of sound system, such as pink noise or sound checks (Client/Venue system).

HEADLESS on Site representative: Dee Riggs

Production:	**"Threshold of Pain" World Tour**
Venue:	**The Royston Hippodrome**
Date/s of Show:	**29th February, 2001**
Client:	**Bleeding Ears Ltd.**
HCP Contact:	**Lee Aison**
Job Reference #:	**546372/2000**
Risk Assessment:	HCP 9
Area / Activity:	Environmental Concerns
Type of Risk:	Workplace Safety

Description of Risk: Low temperature and wet weather

Wet, windy, or icy conditions can all lead to an increased risk of injury through slips and falls, etc.

Persons at Risk: All Crew

Level of risk after implementation of existing controls.

Severity (1 to 10)	2
Likelihood (1 to 10)	5
Frequency (1 to 10)	4
Risk Rating (max 1000)	40 - Minor risk

Existing Controls (provided by Headless Chicken Productions Ltd.)

Crew working in wet conditions have protective clothing

Additional Controls (to be provided by Client / Venue)

HEADLESS Crew should have access to hot liquid refreshment whenever working on site (i.e. 24Hr if necessary).
Provision should be made for grit/salt/sawdust/sand (as required) to make safe icy / slippery / wet surfaces.
No inappropriate clothing requests should be made of the crew.

HEADLESS on Site representative: Dee Riggs

Production:	"Threshold of Pain" World Tour
Venue:	The Royston Hippodrome
Date/s of Show:	29th February, 2001
Client:	Bleeding Ears Ltd.
HCP Contact:	Lee Aison
Job Reference #:	546372/2000

Risk Assessment:	HCP 10
Area / Activity:	Special Effects
Type of Risk:	COSHH

Description of Risk: Smoke, haze fog and mist effects.
Some items of equipment (Smoke Machines, mist makers, dry ice, etc.) require the use of chemicals that in certain conditions could cause a hazard.

| Persons at risk: | All Crew, Clients and Performers |

Level of risk after implementation of existing controls

Severity (1 to 10)	2
Likelihood (1 to 10)	2
Frequency (1 to 10)	5
Risk Rating (max 1000)	20 Minor risk

Existing Controls (provided by Headless Chicken Productions Ltd.)
All Smoke/Ice/Mist Machines supplied by HEADLESS use approved smoke fluids, and operated in accordance with the operating instructions.
Copies of COSHH Data sheets are available on request.

Additional Controls (to be provided by Client / Venue)
Any additional venue, client or local authority requirements should be communicated to the HEADLESS contact prior to the despatch of the equipment.

HEADLESS on Site representative: **Dee Riggs**

Production:	**"Threshold of Pain" World Tour**
Venue:	**The Royston Hippodrome**
Date/s of Show:	**29th February, 2001**
Client:	**Bleeding Ears Ltd.**
HCP Contact:	**Lee Aison**
Job Reference #:	**546372/2000**

Risk Assessment:	**HCP 11**
Area / Activity:	Stage Set
Type of Risk:	Manual Handling

Description of Risk: Moving stage set pieces into place

Stage Set pieces can be large and unwieldy to carry and manoeuvre into place.

Persons at risk: HEADLESS Crew, Venue Crew

Level of risk after implementation of existing controls

Severity (1 to 10)	5
Likelihood (1 to 10)	3
Frequency (1 to 10)	4
Risk Rating (max 1000)	60 Low risk.

Existing Controls (provided by Headless Chicken Productions Ltd.)

The set will be built up from easily transportable pieces wherever possible.
The minimum number of crew will be determined during pre-production and sufficient crew will be provided when required.

Additional Controls (to be provided by Client / Venue)

The venue should ensure that access is clear and any lifts, stairwells, doorways, etc are of an appropriate size to the facilities.

HEADLESS on Site representative: **Dee Riggs**

Production:	"Threshold of Pain" World Tour
Venue:	The Royston Hippodrome
Date/s of Show:	29th February, 2001
Client:	Bleeding Ears Ltd.
HCP Contact:	Lee Aison
Job Reference #:	546372/2000

Risk Assessment:	HCP 12
Area / Activity:	Environmental Concerns
Type of Risk:	Workplace Safety

Description of Risk: Fatigue

Crew work long hours, with little or no access to regular food and drink vending facilities. This increases fatigue and leads to an increased risk of injury.

Persons at risk:	All crew

Level of risk after implementation of existing controls

Severity (1 to 10)	10
Likelihood (1 to 10)	3
Frequency (1 to 10)	6
Risk Rating (max 1000)	180 - Medium risk - needs monitoring

Existing Controls (provided by Headless Chicken Productions Ltd.)

HEADLESS will provide (or arrange for) supplies of hot and cold drinks during any period when crew are working.

HEADLESS will provide (or arrange for) food and/or snacks at any point where the crew are (or will be) unable to break during normal food serving periods.

Additional Controls (to be provided by Client / Venue)

The Venue should be able to provide basic refreshment facilities 24 hours a day. (i.e. water fountains, toilets, etc), as required by the Workplace (Health, Safety and Welfare) Regulations.

HEADLESS on Site representative: **Dee Riggs**

Production:	"Threshold of Pain" World Tour
Venue:	The Royston Hippodrome
Date/s of Show:	29th February, 2001
Client:	Bleeding Ears Ltd.
HCP Contact:	Lee Aison
Job Reference #:	546372/2000
Risk Assessment:	HCP 13
Area / Activity:	Emergency Procedures
Type of Risk:	Fire and First Aid

Description of Risk: Medical emergencies

At any event there is the risk of injury. This risk assessment details the provisions for first aid.

Persons at risk: All persons

Level of risk after implementation of existing controls

Severity (1 to 10)	10
Likelihood (1 to 10)	1
Frequency (1 to 10)	10
Risk Rating (max 1000)	100 - Medium risk - needs monitoring

Existing Controls (provided by Headless Chicken Productions Ltd.)

At least one member of the production who is first aid trained will be present at all times that work is being carried out.

There will be a list of local and venue emergency contact names and addresses issued to all crew at the start of the event.

A fully stocked First Aid box will be kept in the Production office.

The crew will be issued with a copy of the venue's procedures.

Additional Controls (to be provided by Client / Venue)

The Venue should alert the Production Manager to any changes in local/emergency contact numbers, or changes in the Venue's emergency procedures.

The Client should alert the production manager if any extraordinary medical risks are anticipated (e.g. performer with weak heart).

HEADLESS on Site representative: Dee Riggs

Production:	"Threshold of Pain" World Tour
Venue:	The Royston Hippodrome
Date/s of Show:	29th February, 2001
Client:	Bleeding Ears Ltd.
HCP Contact:	Lee Aison
Job Reference #:	546372/2000

Risk Assessment:	HCP 1
Area / Activity:	Emergency Procedures
Type of Risk:	Fire and First Aid

Description of Risk: Show Communications

An emergency may arise at any point during an event. The worst point is during the event itself, when the venue may be dark, full and noisy.

Persons at risk:	All persons

Level of risk after implementation of existing controls

Severity (1 to 10)	10
Likelihood (1 to 10)	1
Frequency (1 to 10)	4
Risk Rating (max 1000)	40 Low risk

Existing Controls (provided by Headless Chicken Productions Ltd.)

Every event will have an intercom system for use by key personnel during the show. This system is likely to be a multi channel system, but any member of the crew can use this system to alert the Production Manager to an emergency or a potential emergency.

Additional Controls (to be provided by Client / Venue)

The venue may wish to request that an intercom station is proved for a responsible person within the Venue's organisation. This may already be provided for other reasons (e.g. house lights).

HEADLESS on Site representative: Dee Riggs

Production:	**"Threshold of Pain" World Tour**
Venue:	**The Royston Hippodrome**
Date/s of Show:	**29th February, 2001**
Client:	**Bleeding Ears Ltd.**
HCP Contact:	**Lee Aison**
Job Reference #:	**546372/2000**

Risk Assessment:	**HCP 15**
Area / Activity:	Emergency Procedures
Type of Risk:	Fire and First Aid

Description of Risk: **Medical emergencies**

At any event there are likely to be an audience. Provision must be made to ensure sufficient first aid cover is provided.

Persons at risk: Members of the public, client's staff

Level of risk after implementation of existing controls

Severity (1 to 10)	10
Likelihood (1 to 10)	2
Frequency (1 to 10)	4
Risk Rating (max 1000)	80 Low risk

Existing Controls (provided by Headless Chicken Productions Ltd.)

The Production Manager will liase with both the Client and the Venue to ascertain both the size of the audience, and the standard provisions for first aid.

In the event of the lack of any other guidelines by the venue, or the client, the Production Manager will refer to the recommendations of the "Event Safety Guide".

Additional Controls (to be provided by Client / Venue)

The venue should alert the Production Manager to any standard arrangements for the health and safety of the audience.

HEADLESS on Site representative: **Dee Riggs**

Production:	"Threshold of Pain" World Tour
Venue:	The Royston Hippodrome
Date/s of Show:	29th February, 2001
Client:	Bleeding Ears Ltd.
HCP Contact:	Lee Aison
Job Reference #:	546372/2000

Risk Assessment:	HCP 16
Area / Activity:	Special Effects
Type of Risk:	Fire and First Aid

Description of Risk: **Ultraviolet light**

Ultraviolet light is sometimes used to produce special effects on stage. Some people have sensitised skin and this may cause an exaggerated sunburn reaction.

Persons at risk: All persons on stage

Level of risk after implementation of existing controls

Severity (1 to 10)	5
Likelihood (1 to 10)	3
Frequency (1 to 10)	5
Risk Rating (max 1000)	75 Low risk

Existing Controls (provided by Headless Chicken Productions Ltd.)

Any lighting effect will be used in accordance with the manufacturers instructions.

Where necessary the control or supply to the "Effect" will be disconnected to prevent accidental use.

All equipment is visually checked for external damage before being used.

Additional Controls (to be provided by Client / Venue)

The client should make any staff that may be affected by this condition, to check if they are aware of having sensitised skin.

HEADLESS on Site representative: **Dee Riggs**

Production:	**"Threshold of Pain" World Tour**
Venue:	**The Royston Hippodrome**
Date/s of Show:	**29th February, 2001**
Client:	**Bleeding Ears Ltd.**
HCP Contact:	**Lee Aison**
Job Reference #:	**546372/2000**

Risk Assessment:	**HCP 17**
Area / Activity:	Lighting
Type of Risk:	Fire and First Aid

Description of Risk: Loss of lighting power or control

The loss of light in a venue could lead to injury due to falls and being trampled on.

| Persons at risk: | All persons |

Level of risk after implementation of existing controls

Severity (1 to 10)	10
Likelihood (1 to 10)	2
Frequency (1 to 10)	1
Risk Rating (max 1000)	20 Low risk

Existing Controls (provided by Headless Chicken Productions Ltd.)

HEADLESS will ensure that the venue possesses an emergency lighting circuit, or will arrange for one to be temporarily installed. Additional emergency lighting will be provided in any temporary area where the standard venue-provided equipment is insufficient.

Additional Controls (to be provided by Client / Venue)

The venue will ensure that the emergency lighting/ house lighting can be activated in the event of a partial power loss that does not affect the emergency circuit. This may require a venue representative being part of the production intercom system.

HEADLESS on Site representative: **Dee Riggs**

Production:	"Threshold of Pain" World Tour
Venue:	The Royston Hippodrome
Date/s of Show:	29th February, 2001
Client:	Bleeding Ears Ltd.
HCP Contact:	Lee Aison
Job Reference #:	546372/2000

Risk Assessment:	HCP 18
Area / Activity:	General
Type of Risk:	Electricity at Work

Description of Risk: Equipotential Earth Bonding

With different contractors setting up different parts of the system, it is possible that conductive metal supporting an electrical load can become live due to an equipment fault.

Persons at risk:	All crew

Level of risk after implementation of existing controls

Severity (1 to 10)	10
Likelihood (1 to 10)	2
Frequency (1 to 10)	5
Risk Rating (max 1000)	100 - Medium risk - needs monitoring

Existing Controls (provided by Headless Chicken Productions Ltd.)

Any extraneous metalwork (e.g. scaffolding) that could become live should be earthed so as to prevent electric shock.

All crew charged with the setting up of electrical equipment should check that any metal object in close vicinity (2.5m) is electrically bonded to earth. (The earth loop impedance may need to be tested if the source of the earth bonding is unclear.)

Additional Controls (to be provided by Client / Venue)

All house fittings that may be used to carry electrical objects should be bonded to earth, and tested as part of the regular general electrical installation inspection.

HEADLESS on Site representative: **Dee Riggs**

Production:	**"Threshold of Pain" World Tour**
Venue:	**The Royston Hippodrome**
Date/s of Show:	**29th February, 2001**
Client:	**Bleeding Ears Ltd.**
HCP Contact:	**Lee Aison**
Job Reference #:	**546372/2000**
Risk Assessment:	**HCP 19**
Area / Activity:	Environmental concerns
Type of Risk:	Workplace Safety

Description of Risk: Wind at outdoor events

High winds can have a dangerous effect on both structures and coverings. These could suffer tearaway damage or collapse.

Persons at risk: All persons

Level of risk after implementation of existing controls

Severity (1 to 10)	10
Likelihood (1 to 10)	2
Frequency (1 to 10)	5
Risk Rating (max 1000)	100 - Medium risk - needs monitoring

Existing Controls (provided by Headless Chicken Productions Ltd.)

HEADLESS crew will monitor weather conditions both locally and predicted.
The company responsible for checking the integrity of the structure will supply maximum wind loading information.
The Production Manager has the authority to cancel an event should the wind become too high.

Additional Controls (to be provided by Client / Venue)

The production office should have access to weather forecast information either by fax, Internet or telephone AT ALL TIMES

HEADLESS on Site representative: **Dee Riggs**

Production:	"Threshold of Pain" World Tour
Venue:	The Royston Hippodrome
Date/s of Show:	29th February, 2001
Client:	Bleeding Ears Ltd.
HCP Contact:	Lee Aison
Job Reference #:	546372/2000
Risk Assessment:	HCP 20
Area / Activity:	Emergency procedures
Type of Risk:	Fire and First Aid

Description of Risk: **Public Announcement (PA) Systems**

In the event of an emergency, the audience may need to be directed towards the emergency exits in a calm manner. It may also be needed for other emergencies, such as requesting a doctor.

Persons at risk: All persons

Level of risk after implementation of existing controls

Severity (1 to 10)	10
Likelihood (1 to 10)	2
Frequency (1 to 10)	4
Risk Rating (max 1000)	80 Low risk

Existing Controls (provided by Headless Chicken Productions Ltd.)

The Production manager will liase with the Venue to verify the existence of a Public Announcement (PA) system with backup power supply.
The Production manager will have a communications path with both the sound engineer and a venue representative to co-ordinate any announcements that have to be made

Additional Controls (to be provided by Client / Venue)

The Venue should ensure that its PA system and its backup power supply is regularly tested, and that the system is properly designed and installed for the building.

HEADLESS on Site representative: **Dee Riggs**

Production:	**"Threshold of Pain" World Tour**
Venue:	**The Royston Hippodrome**
Date/s of Show:	**29th February, 2001**
Client:	**Bleeding Ears Ltd.**
HCP Contact:	**Lee Aison**
Job Reference #:	**546372/2000**

Risk Assessment:	**HCP 21**
Area / Activity:	General
Type of Risk:	Competence and Training

Description of Risk: Competence of contractors.

In order to produce a safe event, Headless Chicken Productions Ltd. has to ensure that their sub-contractors (freelancers and companies) are competent to do the work asked of them.

Persons at risk:	All persons

Level of risk after implementation of existing controls

Severity (1 to 10)	10
Likelihood (1 to 10)	2
Frequency (1 to 10)	2
Risk Rating (max 1000)	40 Low risk

Existing Controls (provided by Headless Chicken Productions Ltd.)

All HEADLESS suppliers undergo a vetting process prior to being asked to participate on a production.

HEADLESS monitors the performance of all suppliers and if doubt arises about their abilities, an immediate reassessment is done by the Production Manager, who has the authority to remove any person or supplier from the event.

Additional Controls (to be provided by Client / Venue)

The venue should ensure that any Venue supplied staff (security, stage crew, house electricians, caterers, etc) are competent to do the work they are performing.

HEADLESS on Site representative: **Dee Riggs**

Production:	"Threshold of Pain" World Tour
Venue:	The Royston Hippodrome
Date/s of Show:	29th February, 2001
Client:	Bleeding Ears Ltd.
HCP Contact:	Lee Aison
Job Reference #:	546372/2000

Risk Assessment:	HCP 1
Area / Activity:	Emergency Procedures
Type of Risk:	Fire and First Aid

Description of Risk: RIDDOR

Any accidents during an event may need to be documented in a number of accident books due to the complexity of the employment paths.

| Persons at risk: | All persons |

Level of risk after implementation of existing controls	
Severity (1 to 10)	N/A
Likelihood (1 to 10)	N/A
Frequency (1 to 10)	N/A
Risk Rating (max 1000)	N/A

Existing Controls (provided by Headless Chicken Productions Ltd.)

Headless Chicken Productions Ltd will provide an "event" accident book which will document ALL accidents that occur as a direct result of the event. This will serve as a "catch all" from where other accident books may be completed, be they venue, contractor or the HEADLESS main book. The Production Manager and Venue manager will liase as to who will perform the reporting duties under RIDDOR, (even though the accident may be another persons responsibility).

Additional Controls (to be provided by Client / Venue)

The venue may require ALL accidents to be reported in their own accident book. In which case the venue should inform the Production Manager immediately, as this book may supersede the requirement for an event accident book.

HEADLESS on Site representative: **Dee Riggs**

Production:	**"Threshold of Pain" World Tour**
Venue:	**The Royston Hippodrome**
Date/s of Show:	**29th February, 2001**
Client:	**Bleeding Ears Ltd.**
HCP Contact:	**Lee Aison**
Job Reference #:	**546372/2000**
Risk Assessment:	**HCP 23**
Area / Activity:	General
Type of Risk:	Lone working & Confined Spaces

Description of Risk: Lone Working

At various points during an event, crew may end up either working alone, or away from any contact with other people.

Persons at risk: All Crew

Level of risk after implementation of existing controls

Severity (1 to 10)	10
Likelihood (1 to 10)	2
Frequency (1 to 10)	5
Risk Rating (max 1000)	100 - Medium risk - needs monitoring

Existing Controls (provided by Headless Chicken Productions Ltd.)

Each group of crew working on a common area (e.g. lighting) will have a crew chief assigned who will be responsible the rest of the group.

The Production team will liase with the crew chiefs at regular intervals to ensure the basic levels of health, such as food and drink requirements.

Additional Controls (to be provided by Client / Venue)

Specific areas within the venue in which it is likely a person may become incommunicado and the inherent risk is higher that normal (e.g. plant room, rigging grid) should be linked to a panic alarm system.

HEADLESS on Site representative: **Dee Riggs**

Production:	"Threshold of Pain" World Tour
Venue:	The Royston Hippodrome
Date/s of Show:	29th February, 2001
Client:	Bleeding Ears Ltd.
HCP Contact:	Lee Aison
Job Reference #:	546372/2000

Risk Assessment:	HCP 24
Area / Activity:	General
Type of Risk:	Explosion

Description of Risk: Compressed Air

Some equipment requires compressed air to operate. This presents a risk of explosion if the air is contained within a pressure vessel.

Persons at risk:	All persons

Level of risk after implementation of existing controls

Severity (1 to 10)	10
Likelihood (1 to 10)	2
Frequency (1 to 10)	2
Risk Rating (max 1000)	40 - Low risk

Existing Controls (provided by Headless Chicken Productions Ltd.)

Wherever possible, pressure vessel systems will be replaced by Hydrovane ™ type compressors.

Any pressure vessels used during an event will be located in a restricted area, remote from the stage and audience.

Additional Controls (to be provided by Client / Venue)

The venue should ensure that any compressed air systems used are clearly marked and protected from accidental damage, and tested regularly.

HEADLESS on Site representative: **Dee Riggs**

Production:	"Threshold of Pain" World Tour
Venue:	The Royston Hippodrome
Date/s of Show:	29th February, 2001
Client:	Bleeding Ears Ltd.
HCP Contact:	Lee Aison
Job Reference #:	546372/2000
Risk Assessment:	HCP 25
Area / Activity:	General
Type of Risk:	CE Marking and Compliance

Description of Risk: Electromagnetic Interference

Radiation emissions from mobile phones and radios can interfere with control equipment.

Persons at risk: All persons

Level of risk after implementation of existing controls

Severity (1 to 10)	10
Likelihood (1 to 10)	1
Frequency (1 to 10)	6
Risk Rating (max 1000)	60 low risk

Existing Controls (provided by Headless Chicken Productions Ltd.)

All equipment supplied to HEADLESS should be manufactured to conform with EMC regulations, Low Voltage and Machinery Directives, as applicable.

During critical operations, crew and audience may be asked to turn off superfluous communications equipment.

Additional Controls (to be provided by Client / Venue)

The venue should ensure that any permanently installed machinery equipment has been checked (and where necessary upgraded) under the Provision and Use of Work Equipment regulations (PUWER) 1998, or the Lifting Operations and Lifting equipment Regulations (LOLER) 1998.

HEADLESS on Site representative: **Dee Riggs**

Production:	"Threshold of Pain" World Tour
Venue:	The Royston Hippodrome
Date/s of Show:	29th February, 2001
Client:	Bleeding Ears Ltd.
HCP Contact:	Lee Aison
Job Reference #:	546372/2000

Risk Assessment:	HCP 1
Area / Activity:	General
Type of Risk:	Electricity at Work

Description of Risk: Hand held devices used by performers.

Any hand held electrical device is a higher risk due to its ease of damage.

Persons at risk:	All performers and crew

Level of risk after implementation of existing controls

Severity (1 to 10)	10
Likelihood (1 to 10)	1
Frequency (1 to 10)	5
Risk Rating (max 1000)	50 Low risk

Existing Controls (provided by Headless Chicken Productions Ltd.)

Any hand held device, or item likely to get wet due to split drinks, etc, and used by a person who is either electrically incompetent, or whose competence is unknown, will either be an extra low voltage System (preferably separated), or will be protected by an RCD.

Any venue/client supplied equipment will be inspected by a competent person before being connected.

Additional Controls (to be provided by Client / Venue)

Any electrical equipment provided by the venue or client (e.g. lectern, overhead projector, etc) should be regularly inspected and tested for damage and degradation.

HEADLESS on Site representative: **Dee Riggs**

Production:	"Threshold of Pain" World Tour
Venue:	The Royston Hippodrome
Date/s of Show:	29th February, 2001
Client:	Bleeding Ears Ltd.
HCP Contact:	Lee Aison
Job Reference #:	546372/2000
Risk Assessment:	HCP 27
Area / Activity:	Special Effects
Type of Risk:	COSHH, Workplace Safety

Description of Risk: Smoke oil, spillage

When a smoke machine is filled with smoke oil, the liquid can spill and cause a slip hazard.

Persons at risk: All persons

Level of risk after implementation of existing controls

Severity (1 to 10)	5
Likelihood (1 to 10)	4
Frequency (1 to 10)	4
Risk Rating (max 1000)	80 Low risk

Existing Controls (provided by Headless Chicken Productions Ltd.)

Smoke machines will be filled in a area away from general access routes.

Before starting the operation, the crew person will ensure that they have sufficient means of preventing a spill (e.g. paper towels, sand, etc) with them.

Additional Controls (to be provided by Client / Venue)

The venue may have a specific area where a spill tray is available for these sort of operations. If so they should alert the Production Manager to its location and safe use.

HEADLESS on Site representative: **Dee Riggs**

Safe connection of single pole (Camlok) three phase power.

- Only one person should be responsible for energising a supply of circuit. It is the responsibility of this person to ensure that a system or circuit can be energised safety.
- Connection to house power is made by bare end tails or lugs and should be carried out by the venue (or generator) electrician.
- Once the tails have been connected, energise the system and check the voltages, ensuring that there are three different phases and that the earth to neutral voltage is satisfactory. If using a generator, ensure that provision has been made to relate the neutral conductor to ground potential. If you do not understand this, STOP.
- De-energise (and where possible secure) the supply, and connect the distribution to the supply. Always follow the "Earth, Neutral, Phase" when connecting single pole connectors. If there is a fault anywhere, you always want to ensure that the first pole connected is the protective conductor, and the next one is the return path. Reverse this sequence when disconnecting.
- Ensure that the correct Camlok colour code has been followed throughout the system, and ensure all breakers and switches are "OFF" before energising the supply.
- Check all indicators and meters for correct operation before starting to energise the next part of the distribution system. Follow this stage by stage method until all required circuits are energised. Never energise a circuit that is not required, or is not yet connected.
- When powering down a system, switch off all breakers and switches from the load end first. This ensures that the larger breakers are not having to disconnect under load, which might cause them to fail prematurely. Switching off in this manner also ensures a safe state for the system in the event of being accidentally re-energised.

Electricity kills.

If you do not understand the implications of this document, do not energise your system. If in doubt,

ASK

Safe working at height (Trusses)

- Anyone who works at height has a responsibility not only to themselves, but to those who may be under them.
- Before starting
  - empty all pockets of any items that could fall out. (e.g. coins, wallet, etc.)
  - Remove any items that you do not need. (e.g. watch, backstage pass, rings etc.)
  - Secure any items that could get caught or cause you to stumble. (e.g. shoelaces, hair, loose shirt etc)
  - Secure any required tools with a lanyard or safety wire to your person.
- Whenever possible, request that the area under where you need to access is kept clear of personnel. If required, use someone on the ground as a moving warning message.
- Use a harness that is appropriate for both the work and the fall arrest-system, with all the appropriate accessories you will require,
- Wherever possible, use two methods of securing yourself. The fall arrest system is only a backup, so if you stop to work, or stop to rest, consider securing yourself there as well.
- Always work in logical steps, never allow yourself to get caught between your work and your safety. Use people on the ground to provide muscle power and legwork wherever possible.

Even a short fall can kill

If you do not understand the implications of this document, do not work at heights. If in doubt,
ASK

Safe manual loading and unloading of trucks

- Always ensure there are sufficient people to lift and manoeuvre the equipment.
- Always ensure that there is one person (and only one person) directing the operation.
- Always be sure of instructions and do not be afraid for clarification. ("Was that on 3 or after 3?")
- Wear gloves to protect your hands from splinters and sharp edges, and consider wearing a back-belt even if you do not have a back problem. Appropriate footwear is very important. There are many forms of protective footwear, and the right type will not only protect your feet if something falls, but can reduce fatigue over the rest of the day.
- Always ensure that there is one person involved in the operation who knows the weight and size of the equipment and flightcases.
- Always try and use a level loading area. If this is not possible, try and position the truck so that gravity will tend to pull any unstable equipment away from those working.
- Always ensure that the working space is free from obstructions and any substances that may cause slips. If necessary split the crew into "wet" and "dry" to avoid mud and water being dragged into the back of the truck on rainy days.
- Always ensure that in icy conditions that there is a supply of salt, sand or grit that can be used in the event of a slippery ramp or floor.
- Use your head. If something looks wrong, it probably is. Do not be afraid to speak out, everyone has a different viewpoint, and everyone is looking at the problem from a different angle.

A back injury can plague you for life

If you do not understand the implications of this document, do not load or unload trucks. If in doubt,
ASK

This is the method statement for "Threshold of Pain" 19th Comeback Tour
Prepared by Lee Aison for Bleeding Ears Ltd.

Date/s of show:	29th February, 2001
Location of Production / Tour:	The Royston Hippodrome
HEADLESS On Site Representative:	Dee Riggs
HEADLESS Reference Number:	546372/2000

Transport:

The Equipment will be transported to the venue using 16 x 40' trailers. The vehicles will require site access from 12:01am on 29th until 06:00am on the 30th.

Loading and Unloading:

The trucks carry ramps so no forklift will be required to unload the truck. 40 stage crew will be required to help push the wheeled flightcases into the venue from the truck, and to remove the lids from the equipment. They will be required for 8 hours 24 crew will be required to assist the loading of the trucks at the end of the event. They will be required for 6 hours.

Rigging:

The equipment will be suspended from a truss based structure which will be hung from 60 points in the roof. All points will have a maximum loading of 1 tonne, and will be secured to the beams by steel wire and chain. The crew will wear safety harnesses and fall arrest equipment when working at height. All rigging equipment will have been regularly tested and inspected as per the requirements of LOLER. The truss will be assembled as per the manufacturers instructions, and checked before being lifted.

Overhead Work:

During the lifting operation, the area beneath the structure will be segregated. It is anticipated that this operation will take 30 minutes. After that, the equipment will take a further 60 minutes to assemble on trusses. After the equipment is set up it will be lifted into its final position and , the area beneath will be safe.

Electrical:

The electrical distribution will be assembled from pre-inspected / pre-tested equipment conforming to BS7909:1998. It will be "plug and socket" type connections, with no live work being required. The distribution equipment will not be powered up until all main connections have been made. We will require a 230v/400v 400A, 3P+N+E supply without RCD into which avenue supplied electrician will connect bare end or lugged tails. In order to assure correct fault discrimination, the temporary distribution equipment is designed to minimise personal injury equipment damage, whilst avoiding the possibilities of the dangers of a complete power failure (e.g. the loss of work lights).

The area around the distribution system must be segregated up to a distance of 1.2m from general access. This is to prevent injury from improper operation of the equipment

Fire and First Aid:

There will be a small first aid box located in the production office for use by the First Aider on the crew. Two CO_2 fire extinguishers will be required at the main control point (front of house) as well as two more in the dimmer area, and by the monitor desk. There are no special precautions that need to be taken other than ones usually taken with electrical equipment.

The production has arranged that the venue will provide adequate first aid arrangements for the general public.

The venue will also be asked to provide the production with details of its emergency and evacuation plans, which will be issued to the crew, and displayed at appropriate points.

Noise:

The PA equipment is capable of extreme levels of sound pressure. However, it will be operated by a competent sound engineer at all times. The SPL will be monitored to ensure it does not go over the guidelines set by the local authority. In addition, the sound engineer will issue warnings prior to any usage of the PA system during the assembly stage (e.g. testing).

Environmental Concerns:

There are no chemicals produced by the equipment, nor waste. UV radiation is generated by lamps inside the luminaires, but under normal use this is filtered out before exiting the lens. The lamp enclosures are interlocked, therefore preventing the exposure of the UV. The crew carry protective clothing including a UV mask, should a problem occur.

Hazardous Chemicals:

There are no chemicals used during the set up, and dismantling of the equipment. There are 10 smoke machines that use a mineral based oil to produce a mist effect in combination with compressed air. This equipment has been tested by the manufacturer who have issued guidelines as to its correct usage.

Name:	
Employee Reference:	
Date of Hire:	

Sheet #:	

COURSE	DATE

Name	**Dee Riggs**
Employee Reference	**1234**
Date of Hire	**1st January 1975**

Sheet #	Four

COURSE	DATE
Fork Lift (Counter Balance)	12/10/1999
Rope Access course	16/1/2000
Manual Handling Course	23/2/2000
Production Technician BTEC	31/3/2000
First Aid	10/4/2000
PAT training course	5/5/2000

	Mack Exellan	Dee Riggs	Lee Alison	Kay Nyre	Howard Elmo				Category	Item
	☑	☑	☑						Driving	Car
	☑									Truck
		☑	☑							Fork lift
		☑							First Aid	Responsible
			☑							Trained
	☑	☑							Electricity	Basic Awareness
	☑									Live Work
	☑									Three Phase
	☑								Hand Power Tools	Compressed Air Tools
	☑									Electric Hand Tools
	☑									Soldering Iron
	☑	☑	☑						Manual Handling	Basic Awareness
	☑									Truck Loading
	☑	☑	☑						IS&T	Basic Phone System
	☑									Reception Switchboard
	☑	☑								Basic Windows
	☑	☑								Network Awareness
	☑	☑							PPE	Basic Awareness
	☑									Welding & Arc Eye
	☑									Painting and Respiration
	☑	☑	☑						Access equipment	Basic awareness
	☑	☑	☑							Working at Heights
	☑									Ladders and towers
	☑									Chain Hoist repair
	☑	☑							Fire	Evacuation procedures
	☑	☑								Fire Fighting Equipment
	☑									Fire Marshall
	☑	☑							H&S	Safety Representative

Employee, Employee, Employee, Employee, Employee, Employee, Employee, Employee, Employee, Employee, Employee, Employee, Employee, etc, etc, etc

example

	Equipment Type	CHEAP Amplifier Rack
	Serial Number or Reference	1468923/80
	Date of purchase	1st January 1980

DATE	INSPECTION	WHO BY
1/1/1980	Initial inspection - OK	FG
12/1/1981	Yearly internal inspection - all OK	SW
25/7/1981	Unit dropped, checked all wiring - OK	RS
23/2/1982	Yearly internal inspection - all OK	FG
16/1/1983	Yearly internal inspection - all OK	FG
13/1/1984	Yearly internal inspection - all OK	SW
12/12/1984	Yearly internal inspection - all OK	RS
13/2/1986	Yearly internal inspection - some loose wires - FIXED	RS
15/1/1987	Yearly internal inspection - all OK	TP
12/1/1988	Yearly internal inspection - signs of burnt wires -FIXED	RS
17/2/1989	Yearly internal inspection - all OK	TP
3/3/1990	Yearly internal inspection - loose wires - FIXED	TP
18/2/1991	Yearly internal inspection - loose screws - FIXED	SW
20/5/1991	Unit returned failed - loose screws and wires - FIXED Suggest bi-annual inspection from now on	EJ
5/1/1992	Yearly internal inspection - loose wires - FIXED	NB
16/7/1992	Bi-annual inspection - Heat damage and bad insulation	NB
18/2/1993	Unit recommended for disposal	TP
31/3/1993	Unit retired from Rental Inventory - Asset to be destroyed	AT

FURTHER READING

Books and leaflets:

HSE Guidance on the Management of Health and Safety at Work Regulations 1992: ISBN 0-7176-0412-8, £5.75, and should include a free update booklet (MISC079) from HSE). *NOTE there should be a new version to go with the new regulations out soon.*

HSE Guidance on the Manual Handling Operations Regulations 1992: ISBN 0-7176-0411-X, £5.75

HSE Guidance on First Aid at Work: ISBN 0-7176-1050-0, £6.75

HSE Approved Code of Practise: General COSHH, Carcinogens and Biological agents regulations 1994: ISBN 0-7176-1308-9, £7.50

Guide to preparing a safety policy statement for a small business: ISBN 0-7176-0424-1, £3.00

HSE Guidance on display screen equipment work: ISBN 0-7176-0410-1, £5.75

Electrical safety at places of entertainment: HSE Guidance note GS50 (free)

Electrical safety for entertainers: HSE IND(G)102L (free)

A Guide to Fire Precautions in Existing Places of Entertainment and Like Premises: Home Office/The Scottish Office: ISBN 0-11-340907-9, £13.00

A Guide to the Reporting of Injuries, Diseases and Dangerous Occurrences Regulations 1995: HSE, ISBN 0-7176-1012-8, £6.95

A Guide to Safety at Sports Grounds: The Stationery Office: ISBN 0-11-300095-2, £15.00

HSE Approved Code of Practice on Workplace health, safety and welfare: ISBN 0-7176-0413-6, £5.75

BS 7909: 1998: Code of Practice for Temporary distribution systems delivering ac electrical supplies for entertainment lighting, technical services and related purposes. (BSI)

Facts for Freelancers: HSE IND(G) 217L (free)

Code of Practice for in-service inspection and testing of electrical equipment: ISBN 0-85296-844-2, IEE, £20.00

BS 7671:1992 Requirements for electrical Installations. IEE Wiring Regulations, 16th Edition

A Guide to the Working Time Regulations, HSE

Safe use of Lifting Equipment Approved Code of Practices and Guidance: ISBN 0-7176-1628-2, HSE, £8.00

Memorandum of Guidance on the Electricity at Work Regulations 1989: ISBN 0-7176-1602-9, HSE, £4.00

The Event Safety Guide: ISBN 0-7176-2453-6, HSE, £20.00.

Safe Use of Work Equipment Approved Code of Practice and Guidance ISBN 0-7176-1626-6, HSE, £8.00.

An introduction to Health and Safety Management for the Live Music Industry: ISBN 0-9530914-0-6, PSA

Personal Protective Equipment at Work, Guidance on Regulations: ISBN 0-7176-0414-2, HSE, £5.75

Temporary demountable structures: Guidance on procurement, design and use (2nd edition): ISBN 1 874266 45 X, ISE, £35.00

Applicable Regulations:
The Health and Safety (Consultation with Employees) Regulations 1996 (S.I. 1996/1513)

Working Time Regulations 1998 (SI 1998/1833)

The Children (Protection at Work) Regulations 1998 (S.I. 1998/276)

The Children (Protection at Work) Regulations 2000 (SI 2000/1333)

The Health and Safety (First-Aid) Regulations 1981 (SI 1981/917)

The Fire Precautions (Workplace) Regulations 1997
(SI 1997/1840) (amended by S.I. 1999/1877.)

The Control of Substances Hazardous to Health Regulations 1999
(SI 1999/437)

The Highly Flammable Liquids and Liquefied Petroleum Gases Regulations 1972 (SI 1972/917)

The Provision and Use of Work Equipment Regulations 1998
(SI 1998/2306)

The Lifting Operations and Lifting Equipment Regulations 1998
(SI 1998/2307)

The Health and Safety (Display Equipment) Regulations 1992
(SI 1992/2792)

Reporting of Injuries, Diseases and Dangerous Occurrences Regulations 1995

The Workplace (health, safety and welfare) Regulations 1992
(SI 1992/3004)

Electricity at Work Regulations 1989 (SI 1989/635)

Manual Handling Operations Regulations 1992

Personal Protective Equipment at Work regulations: 1992
(SI1992/2966)

The Management of Health and Safety at Work Regulations 1999
(SI 1999/3242)

Noise at Work Regulations 1989

Useful Addresses
The UK Public Sector Information Web Site.
http://www.open.gov.uk/

NOTE: This site is a useful gateway to ALL government bodies. It contains a search engine, indices and a "what's new" information update page.

Health and Safety Executive (HSE)
http://www.open.gov.uk/hse/hsehome.htm
HSE Books, PO Box 1999, Sudbury, Suffolk CO10 6FS
Telephone 01787 881165
Fax: 01787 313995

British Standards Institute (BSI)
389 Chiswick High Road, London, W4 4AL
Telephone: 020 8996 7000
http://www.bsi.org/

The Stationery Office
Publications centre (mail, telephone and fax orders only),
PO Box 276, London SW8 5DT
Telephone (Enquiries): 020 7873 0011
Telephone (Orders): 020 7873 9090
http://www.the-stationery-office.co.uk/

The Production Services Association (PSA)
Unit 3a, Endeavour House, 2 Cambridge Road,
Kingston Upon Thames, Surrey KT1 3JU
Telephone 020 8392 0180
Fax: 020 8541 0247
http://www.psa.org.uk/

The Professional Lighting And Sound Association (PLASA)
38 St Leonards Road, Eastbourne, East Sussex BN21 3UT, UK
Telephone: 01323 410335
Fax: 01323 646905
http://www.plasa.org/

Her Majesty's Stationery Office (HMSO)

The Home Office
Telephone (Publications): 020 7273 3072
http://www.homeoffice.gov.uk/

The Department of Trade and Industry (DTI)
DTI Enquiry Unit, 1 Victoria Street, London SW1H 0ET
http://www.dti.gov.uk/

The Institution of Structural Engineers (ISE)
11 Upper Belgrave Street, London SW1X 8BH
Telephone: 020 7235 4535
Fax: 020 7235 4294
http://www.istructe.org.uk/

Institute of Electrical Engineers (IEE)
Savoy Place, London, WC2R 0BL, UK
Telephone: 020 7240 1871
Fax: 020 7240 7735
http://www.iee.org.uk/

ENTERTAINMENT TECHNOLOGY PRESS

FREE SUBSCRIPTION SERVICE

Keeping Up To Date with

A Practical Guide
to Health and Safety
in the Entertainment Industry

Entertainment Technology Press titles are continually up-dated, and all changes and additions are listed in date order in the relevant dedicated area of the publisher's website. Simply go to the front page of www.etnow.com and click on the BOOKS button. From there you can locate the title and be connected through to the latest information and services related to the publication.

The author of A Practical Guide to Health and Safety in the Entertainment Industry is a director of Supporting Role Limited and companies or individuals wishing to find out more about the company's services can visit their website at: http://www.supporting-role.co.uk/